'Here's the deal. You for your brother. Straight across!'

Maggie gasped. 'You can't be serious.'

He shrugged. 'You or him. Which is it?'

'What do you want from me?' she whispered.

His eyes narrowed. 'I dreamt about the day that I'd have you in my power. You won't find me so easy to shove from your arms this time. A red-haired witch who pretended she was going to share her magic until she disappeared into a puff of smoke.' He studied her in silence a few moments before continuing, 'You won't disappear this time, Red. This time I've caught you and I have no intention of letting you escape. We're getting married.'

'Married! But marriage is for ever.'

'Exactly.'

ONE RECKLESS MOMENT

BY

JEANNE ALLAN

MILLS & BOON LIMITED
ETON HOUSE   18-24 PARADISE ROAD
RICHMOND   SURREY   TW9 1SR

First published in Great Britain 1988
by Mills & Boon Limited

© Jeanne Allan 1988

Australian copyright 1988
Philippine copyright 1988
This edition 1988

ISBN 0 263 76154 1

Set in English Times 11 on 11 pt.
01 – 8812 – 47841

Typeset in Great Britain by JCL Graphics, Bristol

Made and printed in Great Britain

CHAPTER ONE

'IT was a dark and stormy night,' Maggie quoted melodramatically to Archie, mirth building up within her as she glanced in the car's rear-view mirror. Archie looked almost human with a pained expression of disgust on his face at her frivolous remark but his obvious displeasure could no more dampen her spirits than could the frightful weather which had prompted the remark. 'I'm free, Archie! Free! Do you know how long it's been since I haven't had a list of forty thousand things to do that needed to be done yesterday? Okay,' she admitted, 'so the lists are still around, but at least they're home on the kitchen table along with the paint and wallpaper. And I'm here. Here in Colorado with nothing more on my mind than having a great and glorious vacation. Imagine. Three meals a day cooked by someone else. Slushing down the snowy slopes of Aspen. Well, maybe slushing isn't the right word,' she conceded as the dog whined, 'especially since I'll be cross-country skiing, but you know I can't afford lift-tickets. Don't be such a spoilsport or the next time I go somewhere, it'll be the kennel for you.'

Ignoring her threat, the large red Irish setter circled restlessly on the back seat and again whined uneasily. 'Easy, fella, I know you don't like the snow.' She reached back and patted his red head. 'It won't be long now. According to the map, Aspen is only about thirty-eight miles from Twin Lakes, and we passed through there a couple of minutes ago.'

5

Her comments failed to reassure the dog and he continued to pace back and forth on the car seat, his movements as regular as the wipers sweeping broadly across the windscreen. And about as effective. There was a certain amount of justification for Archie's fears. He had lived his entire life in Arizona and the present weather must seem very foreign to him. Maggie blinked her eyes and opened them wide. Looking into the swirl of snowflakes pin-pointed by the car lights was having a mesmerising effect on her. If she wasn't careful she would end up in the ditch, not an appealing prospect at seven o'clock at night, especially since she hadn't seen a lighted window since shortly after leaving the small community of Twin Lakes. For the first time disquiet began to nibble away at the edges of her euphoria, and she wondered uneasily if she should turn around and go back to Twin Lakes and spend the night at the inn. Finishing her journey in the morning would be the sensible thing to do.

'And Maggie Russell is aways sensible,' she said aloud in a mocking voice. Which immediately settled the question of returning to the inn. Hadn't she resolved to leave the sensible Maggie at home with the wallpaper and the paint? On to Aspen!

Ignoring the anxious snuffling behind her, she switched the wipers to their highest speed. They fought a valiant, but steadily losing, battle against the rapidly falling wet snow. Slowing her speed to a snail's pace, Maggie hugged the middle of the road, grateful for the lack of oncoming traffic. Her headlights barely penetrated the storm to delineate the narrow, curving road, picking out stark silhouettes of tall pines. Looming on either side of her were tall moutains, felt more than seen. The entire outside world was black, an oppressive darkness given a ghostly aspect by the mad swirls of blowing snow.

Earlier the snow had melted as it encountered the pavement but now Maggie sensed that the moisture on the road's surface was turning to ice beneath the wheels of her small car. A sudden, ferocious gust of wind shook the car, and Archie, who had left off whining while continuing to pace, once more began audibly expressing his displeasure A cold feeling which she could no longer blame on an ineffective car-heater began settling into the pit of Maggie's stomach.

Off to her right, as welcome as it was unexpected, a small yellow square of light shone briefly through the trees, comforting proof that there was at least one other human inhabitant of these dark woods. For some reason, the thought of a small family sitting cosily around a warm fireplace popping corn and telling stories cheered Maggie up. Bayard and his friends were no doubt similarly employed. She could imagine the surprise on their faces when she knocked at the door of their rented flat.

The whine from the back seat changed to a familiar, urgent intensity. 'Oh no, Archie. Not now. You'll have to wait until we get to Aspen. I don't dare stop now to let you out.' Turning slightly in her seat, Maggie reached back and patted the dog. 'It won't be long,' she promised. Archie barked, a sharp note of warning. By the time Maggie turned back to face the road and saw the barricades it was too late. In panic she slammed down hard on the brake pedal. A heavy thump against the back of her seat told her that Archie had been sent flying even as the car erratically swerved and slid sideways, slowly and inevitably towards the wooden barricades.

How she missed them would always be a mystery to her. Not that the car's final resting place was much of an improvement. With the front end buried in a huge pile of snow, it didn't take a genius to realise that she wasn't going anywhere. Even in the darkness she could see that the road beyond the barricades was unploughed, the snow deep and undisturbed. No help could be expected from that direction. Or the other, for that matter. Why would anyone drive along a road that obviously went nowhere? And why in the world was the road closed? And rather permanently, from the looks of things. It was a state highway, for heaven's sake. Why hadn't there been warning signs?

Belatedly Maggie cursed the wave of rebellion that had caught her in a weak moment of self-pity and carried her precipitately into the mountains of Colorado. Too many years of self-restraint, too many years of shouldering tremendous burdens of responsibility, too many years of dependable behaviour had weighed her down until the drudgery of painting the kitchen while the rest of the world played had been the proverbial straw and something inside her had snapped, irresistibly propelling her into actions totally alien to her normal, sensible behaviour. Now, it appeared, she was to pay the price for her one uncharacteristic moment of recklessness.

A moist nose nudging her neck forcibly reminded her that she wasn't the only one paying the price. 'Well, boy,' she said shakily, 'you said you wanted to stop.' Shivering in the rapidly chilling car, she thrust her arms in her jacket and snapped the lead on Archie. The wind had begun to blow, arctic gusts that fought her efforts to open the car door. Finally succeeding, she was unpleasantly surprised at the depth of the snow. The flakes were larger now and falling heavily. Archie didn't like the unfamiliar snow and refused to abandon the car in spite of Maggie's violent tugs on his lead. 'C'mon, Archie,' she pleaded. 'A quick trip around the car and then we can get back inside.' In a sudden, decisive move that caught Maggie totally by surprise, the large setter lunged from the car with unexpected alacrity, knocking her headlong into the snow. Jerking the lead from her hand, he disappeared into the darkness.

Maggie struggled to her feet, brushing with futile gestures at the snow clinging to her clothes and yelling loudly for Archie to return. The wind seemed to tear her voice from her throat, remorselessly swallowing her cries. Straining to pick up the sound of Archie's barking, she heard only the howling of the wind. Fear clutched at her throat. What if Archie didn't come back? His wanderlust career was well documented. A gate not firmly latched, a door accidently left ajar—all were invitations that the large setter took immediate advantage of, sometimes not returning for days in spite of Maggie's efforts to track him.

She looked down at the snow. Archie's large footprints led directly to the woods. What kind of wild creatures awaited him there? He was a lover, not a fighter. And traps . . . Maggie had read about the brutal traps set by unscrupulous hunters for beaver and bears that snared unwary dogs. The thought of Archie captured in such a trap, with a broken leg or worse, sent a sickening shaft of fear directly to Maggie's stomach and lent new urgency to her voice. The large red dog failed to appear as his footprints slowly filled with snow. Soon the storm would erase them as if they had never been. Maggie stood irresolute, shivering with cold and alarm. Archie depended on her. If anything happened to him she would have no one to blame but herself. Her headlong retreat from her chores, her blithe refusal to stop for the night back at the last town . . . why hadn't she wrapped Archie's lead firmly around her wrist?

His trail was growing dimmer. Soon it would be impossible to track him. She glanced uneasily about her. The car represented security and at least a small measure of warmth. The woods . . . tales of people wandering until they froze to death in the cold filtered through her mind. She started to get back into the car, then hesitated, her hand on the door. She couldn't abandon Archie. She would follow his tracks just a little way into the woods. If he didn't hear her calling and reappear shortly, she could follow her own trail back to the car.

She had taken only two steps when she remembered the skis fastened to the back of the car. The teacher who had lent them to her had assured her that cross-country skiing was as natural as walking. 'Just slide one foot forward and then the other, balancing on your poles,' he had instructed. It had seemed so easy in his living-room. Maggie eyed the rapidly falling snow and reasoned that she could cover more ground in a shorter period of time if she wore the skis. Long minutes of struggling with the unfamiliar bindings with hands made clumsy by the numbing cold were required before the long, skinny boards were finally attached to the special boots and she slid awkwardly into the woods.

An hour later she knew that donning the skis had

been a mistake. Soaking wet from frequent tumbles in the snow, she was shivering uncontrollably. The hard, icy bits of snow that pelted from the sky had ceased to sting a face numbed by the chilling wind and she no longer bothered to wipe the moisture from eyes and nose. Tracking Archie through the black woods had proved impossible, and struggling through the dense trees that attacked her with whip-like branches only compounded her lack of skill. When she had become ensnared in a small thicket of aspen, she had admitted defeat and turned back towards her car. Only a few feet of following her back trail were needed before the foolhardy nature of her actions was sickeningly apparent. The heavy snowfall combined with her slow progress had erased her back trail. She had no idea in which direction her car lay. Leaning over the ski poles, Maggie gasped for air, each breath searing torture to lungs unable to cope with the lack of oxygen at the unfamiliar altitude. Her head hurt unendurably. She was so very tired. If only Archie hadn't abandoned her. People were always professing to love you and then they abandoned you.

'You silly little goose,' her mother's light teasing voice broke into her thoughts. 'Why are you standing out there in the cold? Come inside.' The lit doorway framed her smiling figure. 'I've made some popcorn and your father is ready to read the next chapter of *The Call of the Wild*.'

'I hate that story. Everybody dies.'

'Everybody has to die some time.' Her father stood behind her mother. 'You know that, Maggie,' he added gently.

'No, I don't want to hear it!' she screamed, her eyes squeezed tightly shut, her mittened hands covering her ears. There was no answer. Maggie opened her eyes. The doorway was gone, her parents with it. 'Mama, Daddy, come back. Don't leave me. Please.' She started to cry.

'You don't have time to feel sorry for yourself. Not with the children to look after,' Nana said briskly.

Maggie looked up in surprise. Nana stood there, a bulwark of security in her snowy white apron. Maggie could smell the cookies baking in the kitchen behind her grandmother. 'Nana!' She lunged clumsily forward. Her grandmother faded away leaving a small, snow-covered aspen tree standing in her place. 'Nana, don't you leave me, too. Please. I'm so cold.' Tears flowed down her face.

'Why are you crying, Maggie? You never cry.' Julie's soft, hesitating voice was barely audible above the howling wind. 'Are you hurt?'

'No. I'm just so cold and so tired.'

'Why don't you lie down and take a nap?' The bed Julie patted was piled high with white quilts.

Awkwardly Maggie turned the unwieldy skis towards her sister. Julie giggled and backed away from the bed. 'No!' Maggie cried, struggling to catch Julie before she disappeared. Snow clung to her skis in heavy clumps and her legs were frozen blocks of ice. Just as she reached the bed its outline wavered in front of her eyes, transforming the bed into a huge boulder, mounded with snow. Before Maggie's mind could grasp this latest disappointment, her left ski met disaster. The boulder had acted as a windbreak during the snowfall causing snow to drift around it, leaving a large hole directly in front of the rock. Maggie's ski slid swiftly into the hole, and she plunged to the ground, her left ski wedged firmly against the boulder, her right leg and ski crossed beneath her left. She didn't have the energy to untangle the mess. She would just rest awhile.

'Why are you sleeping on the floor?'

Maggie opened her eyes. Julie was perched on the bed, looking down on her. 'I'm cold.' She couldn't keep her eyes open any longer.

A sharp noise. The alarm clock. Time to get up and get ready for work, but she was so tired. Groaning she opened her eyes. Archie stood beside her, barking sharply. 'Archie, you can't need to go out now. It's still dark. Wait until morning.' She was so cold. Her eyes closed. Bayard would let Archie out. She could sleep a few minutes longer.

'Anything broken?'

Why was Bayard snapping at her? Archie must have got him up. It wasn't as if she slept late every day.

'Can you stand?'

'Go away, Bayard. Let me sleep.'

'What are you doing here?'

Maggie giggled. 'Don't be silly. Where else would I sleep?'

'What's your name?'

Why was Bayard being so stupid? Was he still mad because she had stayed at home to paint? 'The little red hen.' She giggled again. 'I'll do it myself.'

'Whatever you say, Red. I don't think anything is broken.'

Why did Bayard keep talking about being broken? Of course. Their fight. 'You were right,' she conceded. 'There. I've admitted it. Can I go back to sleep now?'

'In a minute, Red.'

Red? She wasn't going to paint the kitchen red. She

struggled to open her eyes. Bayard had his back to her, poking at a roaring fire. She knew he would have a fire. What had he thought when she had knocked on his door? 'I'll bet you were surprised to see me,' she said drowsily. She would explain in the morning. Just now she was too tired for explanations. And too cold.

Warmth. Heavenly warmth. Forcing open reluctant eyelids, Maggie gazed around an unfamiliar, darkened room. The single window within her field of vision was curtained, but a feeble gleam of light stole through the centre gap. The curtain moved restlessly and then she heard the wind. An eerie, howling wind that seemed to shake the foundations of the room. Obviously the storm had developed into a full-scale blizzard. No one would expect her to ski in a blizzard. She could sleep all day.

Maggie snuggled contentedly into the warm cocoon of blankets. Her eyes closed. A hint of wood smoke eddied past her cold nose. She hoped that Bayard had remembered to close the fireplace damper. There was a whistling sound near her ear. The wind must be trying to invade the room by way of the chimney.

Odd how she couldn't remember whether or not Bayard had been surprised to see her last night. After their argument, Maggie would have been the last person he had expected. Funny how he thought she was planning to paint the kitchen red. Hadn't he seen the yellow paint before he left? Maybe not. He had been so furious with her refusal to go to Colorado with him. Always the martyr, he had sneered. He didn't seem to understand that someone had to keep her nose to the grindstone. If Maggie hadn't, what would have happened to him and Julie? No. She wouldn't dwell on such self-pitying thoughts. She was here to have fun, to forget her responsibilities, if only for a short time. Bayard was right. She had been taking herself too seriously.

And it was heavenly to lie in bed. No alarm clock. No conscience jabbing her to get up and into the kitchen to make breakfast. For once to lose herself to the siren songs of sloth and laziness. She stretched luxuriously in the warm bed. Or at least she tried. A solid bulk at her back, a lead weight across her stomach restricted her movements. For the first time she was aware of the sound of breathing close at hand. The whistling sound came not from a fireplace but from a living creature snoring lightly in her ear.

Archie. He had taken advantage of her exhaustion last night and crawled on to her bed. No doubt the floor of the flat was much colder than he was accustomed to, and she had been unable to carry his dog bed with her when she left the car. A puzzled frown wrinkled her brow while a murky, disquieting thought teased at the edges of her consciousness. Something she should remember about her car. Archie shifted, throwing more of his weight across her legs. The half-formed thought fled to be replaced by indignation. Archie knew very well that he was not allowed on the furniture. Especially not on her bed.

She nudged him with her hips. 'Get off the bed.' The setter's heavy breathing continued unabated. Maggie shoved harder. 'Get off the bed, you big oaf.'

'Good morning to you, too, Red.'

The low, amused voice in her ear was an electrifying shock. Jerking her head about in stunned disbelief, Maggie stared with horror at the unfamiliar face that shared her pillow. Shaggy blue-black hair tumbled down to dark, heavy eyebrows over sleepy blue eyes. The look in those eyes sent Maggie's temperature soaring. The sensual appeal of a cleft in his chin the size of the Grand Canyon was not lessened by the dark stubble that covered the lower third of his face. 'You need a shave,' she croaked.

'I hope that's not a serious impediment,' he drawled, amusement flickering in his eyes.

'To what?' Maggie asked, hypnotised by the face mere inches from hers on the pillow.

'This,' he said smoothly, and then there were no inches between them at all.

Maggie was too shocked to do other than lie there, her limbs pipes of lead unconnected to her brain. His mouth was warm against hers.

He leaned back with a small sigh. 'You're supposed to respond, Red.'

'Why do you keep calling me Red?'

He glanced at her hair and grinned. 'Surely its obvious. Besides, last night you told me that was your name.'

'Last night?' she echoed stupidly. 'Who are you?'

At her question, a shutter seemed to close over his eyes. There was no amusement now. Only watchful wariness. 'Don't you know?'

Wordlessly she shook her head, helpless to break the thrall of his intense blue eyes. Her gaze was drawn to his lips. Firm lips, for all they had felt so soft, so gentle. She touched her upper lip with the tip of her tongue. It didn't feel the same. Perhaps . . . He seemed to read her mind. Hurriedly she closed her eyes against the flame that flared in his. The gentle investigation of the first kiss was replaced by a bold exploration of her mouth that left her weak and panting. The look of smug satisfaction on his face told her that he was used to having that effect on women.

If she hadn't been dreaming, she would have smacked him. But since she was . . . Her eyes flickered closed. Incredible how a dream could seem so real. Not only was her heart pounding, but she could even imagine that she felt his heart beating against her chest. Just as she could feel the heat from his body, smell the musky, pleasing odour of his skin. The texture of the tongue curled around hers excited her more than any dream had a right to do. In a moment of pique, she withdrew her lips from his. No dream should have the power to unsettle her so.

She remembered seeing her parents and her grandmother last night during the snow. She kept her eyes squeezed tightly shut. She didn't want to know where she was. He was trying to trick her into thinking that she was in heaven. Only she knew better. It was the other place. That was why she felt so oddly incomplete. So . . . so haunted by strange and unfamiliar longings. And warm. So very warm. 'I'm dead, aren't I?'

He gave a shout of laughter.

Her eyes shot open in surprise. Did they laugh down there?

The laughter faded from the apparition's face to be replaced by a look of concern. 'Not that it wasn't close. Too close. What were you doing wandering around in the snow at that time of night out in the middle of nowhere?'

'You mean I'm not dreaming?' With a trembling hand she reached up and touched his face. The stubble on his cheek rasped against her fingers. 'You are real.'

A cocky grin lit up his face. 'I was the last time I checked.'

Shock swept through Maggie's body. What was she doing in bed with a strange man? A man she had let kiss her. Even worse, a man she had kissed back. Sitting up, she thrust aside the blankets, seeking to escape. The sight that greeted her was worse, far worse than anything that she could ever have imagined. Both she and the man were stark naked. With a gasp of horror she yanked the covers up around her neck. She could feel the crimson tide that surged up her entire body.

'Sorry,' he said lazily. 'I guess I kind of forgot about our lack of clothing.'

'Why are we . . . we . . . you know . . . Who are you?' Maggie whispered shakily.

With a barely perceptible pause he answered, 'Nick Peters.'

He was lying. Maggie knew it as surely as if he had failed a lie-detector test. Who was he? Why was he lying to her?

He reached over and curled a lock of red hair around a long shapely finger. 'I guess you don't remember much about last night, do you, Red?'

'Don't call me Red,' she flashed automatically. Then his words sank in with dismaying significance as she recalled their unclothed state. Swallowing hard against the horrible suspicion that rose in her throat, she forced herself to ask, 'What exactly happened last night?'

He lay back on the pillow, his arms crossed beneath his head. A frosty smile failed to reach his eyes. 'It's obvious what conclusion you've come to.'

Maggie barely heard his answer. The covers had

slid down to his waist when she had made her abortive leap from bed, and the sight of all that masculine nudity within inches of her own body overwhelmed her. Without stopping to think, she reached over and pushed the blanket up to his chin. Unfortunately at the same time, she lost her death grip on the blankets covering her and they dropped to her waist. Panicked by her own nudity she stood up and whipped the covers from the bed, flinging them protectively about her body. Too late she remembered that she wasn't the only one not wearing clothes. The naked, recumbent body on the bed was too much for her befuddled brain to cope with and she dashed from the room in shock. Deep, bellowing laughter followed her.

One look out of the door into the white, swirling landscape convinced Maggie that there was no escape in that direction. Looking around what proved to be a large living-room disclosed no clothing. She had to remain calm. There must be a logical explanation for all this. There must be. Wrapping the blankets even more snugly around her, she sat apprehensively on a straight-backed wooden chair, staring nervously at the open bedroom door. The laughter had stopped. Well, almost. A few chuckles still rang out now and again punctuating the sounds of a man dressing. Was he laughing because he knew that she was in his power? Another gust of wind shook the cabin and Maggie swallowed a sob. Would she be safer braving the rigours of the storm?

Archie lay sound asleep on a dark rug in front of the cold hearth. 'Some protection you are,' she hissed at the setter, poking him with a bare toe. 'I suppose that's why they say a dog is a *man's* best friend.'

She stiffened as the man emerged from the bedroom. At least one of them was dressed. Standing, he was taller than she had realised. Several inches over six feet. His lips twitched as soon as he saw her sitting there on the edge of the chair. He was still laughing at her. Fear fled before fury. 'It's not funny.'

'If you could have seen the look on your face after you stole the blanket.' Sensing her anger he tried to swallow his laughter, succeeding only in choking.

'Very amusing, I'm sure,' Maggie snapped.

'Look. I'm sorry. Let's start all over again. My name is Nick Peters and you're . . .?' He started towards her.

Maggie stood up in alarm, a hasty manoeuvre that caused her to trip over the blankets, yanking them low enough to expose one rounded breast.

Nick Peters immediately turned his back on her. At least he had the decency to do that, Maggie thought, somewhat appeased until she heard the strangled noises coming from his throat. 'Your clothes are still wet, but I put a sweater and some jeans on the bed if you want to get out of . . .' Choking, he had to pause to get his voice under control. 'If you want to wear something other than that blanket.' He turned around.

Maggie edged away. 'I'm glad one of us is finding this situation funny.' She winced as she banged her hip against a small table.

'Watch out!' He sprang towards a teetering lamp.

Backing up to avoid his outstretched hand she bumped into the sofa and promptly fell headlong on to it, the blankets tangling around her bare legs.

He choked again, saw her struggle to cover her legs and gave up his own battle. Brushing aside her feet he sank limply to the end of the sofa and surrendered to spasms of laughter. Maggie eyed him doubtfully. Would a raving maniac laugh that spontaneously? She had no knowledge of insanity but, if he were truly crazy, shouldn't there be some hint of madness in his eyes? His blue eyes brimmed with amusement. With visible effort, he brought his laughter under control. 'I'm sorry. I guess that isn't very humorous to you.'

'Not very,' she bit out. Striving to maintain some shred of dignity she stood up. 'I think I'll get dressed now.' Her nose in the air, Maggie sailed past him to the bedroom. Unfortunately she failed to see that Archie was awake and stretching his long body in the normal morning ritual. The setter yelped in agony as she stepped on his paw. Abandoning dignity, she ran for the bedroom, hastily slamming the door to shut out the cacophony of howls and laughter left in her wake.

Muttering under her breath, Maggie tied her hair at the nape of her neck with the shoelace she had pulled from one of his shoes. He hadn't lied when he had said her clothes were still wet. No wonder. Abandoned as they were in a heap on the floor, how could he expect them to dry? Dressing, she tried to ignore the thousands of questions that were crying to be answered. Like, where was she? How did she get here? Where was Bayard? Who was the man who called himself Nick Peters? And why were the two of them naked in bed together?

At least she wasn't naked any more. From the way it fitted her, the heavy blue turtleneck was obviously his. Not that she minded something that covered her from her neck to her knees. The jeans were a perfect fit. Not his, but women's jeans. His girlfriend's, no doubt. She frowned at her reflection in the mirror. Why was she so sure that there wasn't a Mrs Nick Peters? She looked around the bedroom. Shaker pegs lining the walls held a variety of outdoor equipment and masculine apparel, from fishing poles and nets to a red buffalo tartan shirt that had seen a number of years of wear. A profusion of baseball caps and cowboy hats hung on a brass stand in one corner while a heavy terry-cloth robe and blue checked nightshirt dangled from a hook on the back of the door. Her eyes travelled back to the nightshirt in wonder. It was hard to imagine such a plebeian garment on him.

Maggie put down his brush with trembling hands. She had to go out and face him some time. She had to know what had happened. Didn't she? Turning too quickly away from the mirror caused her muscles to scream in protest. Why was she so sore? Or was that another question she didn't really want answered?

A loud thumping on the bedroom door sent her heart leaping to her throat. She had to swallow twice before she managed to croak, 'What . . . what is it?'

'Breakfast.'

When had she eaten last? The hamburger at Sante Fe? Suddenly, in spite of her fears, she was ravenous.

The door opened and he poked his head inside. 'You OK?'

She nodded, her heart stopped between beats. His dark head was so threateningly masculine. Who was he?

He frowned at her hair.

'I couldn't find anything else,' she said defensively, touching the shoelace.

Ignoring her explanation, he walked over to an old

pine dresser and pulled out a pair of grey wool socks. 'You'd never be able to manage in any of my shoes, but these should work.'

'Thank you.' She accepted them primly from his outstretched hand.

His eyes danced with delight. 'We're making progress. You didn't back up. Oops.' He threw his hands up into the air in a mocking gesture of surrender as she angrily opened her mouth. 'I keep forgetting about the colour of your hair, Red.'

'Maggie,' she said stiffly.

'Maggie?'

'My name is not Red; it's Maggie.'

A grin crinkled the skin around his eyes. 'I kinda like Red myself.'

'Fortunately, my parents didn't think to consult you when I was born.' Those strange feelings in the pit of her stomach had nothing to do with his laughing eyes. Hunger pangs. That was all they were.

'Maggie what?'

She looked at him squarely in the eye. 'I'll tell you when you tell me your name.'

He looked at her in surprise. 'I've already told you. Nick Peters.'

'I may have been stupid enough to spend the night with you, Mr Peters,' she mockingly emphasised his last name, 'but I've had enough experience with teenagers to know when I'm being lied to.'

Her words wiped the grin from his lips and he scrutinised her face through narrowed eyes. A cold shiver of fear raced up her back at the sudden feeling she had of hostility directed towards her. It was stupid to challenge this man.

'Are you a teacher?' he asked in a clipped voice.

'No . . . a . . . a librarian,' she stammered.

Unexpectedly he laughed. 'That's so crazy, I almost believe you.' He walked out of the room.

'Why shouldn't you believe me?' she asked indignantly, as she followed him into the kitchen, hopping first on one foot and then on the other as she struggled into the heavy stockings. 'It's true.'

He put a plate of pancakes and bacon on the table and motioned for her to sit down. 'And I suppose it's entirely accidental that you ended up in my bed?'

Maggie frowned. 'I don't know how I ended up there.'

'C'mon, Red. Ever since that damned article came out I've been hounded to death. I have to admit that your ploy has been the cleverest yet.'

Maggie stared at him, fork poised half-way to her mouth. 'My ploy?'

'To meet "one of Colorado's most eligible bachelors",' he quoted bitterly. 'That innocent expression of yours is good, damned good, but if you didn't come waltzing through that storm last night on purpose just to get snowed in with me, then I'm a monkey's uncle.'

Maggie choked on her bacon. 'That does it. You are crazy. There's a raging blizzard outside; I have no idea where I am, and to top it off, I'm shut in with a raving maniac. Even worse, I spent the night with a raving maniac.' Tamping down her rising fears, she put on a false front of courage, adding, she hoped, with conviction, 'I'm a black belt in judo, you know.'

The effect of her statement was not all that she desired. He was drinking coffee and choked at her words. 'A judo expert and a librarian. An interesting combination,' he said, wiping up spilled coffee. 'You wouldn't happen to be a newspaper reporter, too, would you?'

'I told you. I'm a librarian.'

'And you just happened to be out for a little evening jaunt on skis and just happened to run across my cabin and just happened to conveniently get into trouble about one hundred yards from it,' he said in disgust.

'I had a small accident,' she said defensively. 'On my way to Aspen.'

'Tell me another one, Red. I thought librarians had to know how to read.'

'What's that supposed to mean?'

'There are signs all over that Independence Pass is closed for the winter. I suppose you're going to tell me that you didn't see them.'

'Of course I saw them. So what?'

'So what? You have to cross Independence Pass to get to Aspen from here.'

She stared at him in dismay. 'I thought that the signs referred to some hiking trail. It doesn't say a thing on my map about the road being closed. Who ever heard of closing a whole highway just because of a little snow?'

'More than a little snow,' he said drily. 'As you discovered for yourself last night. What kind of accident?'

Maggie shrugged. 'Nothing serious. I just kind of slid off the road at the barricades.' Not for anything would she admit that she had been talking to Archie instead of paying attention to the road ahead of her.

'Where are you from?'

'Arizona.'

'It figures,' he said, disapproval coating his words. 'A damn tourist. You people from down south never show the proper respect for Colorado winters. I'll bet you didn't even have snowchains.'

'They're not exactly a necessity in my part of the country,' Maggie retorted, refusing to acknowledge that she had been at fault.

'What were you doing cross-country skiing at that time of night, or is that normal Arizona behaviour, too?'

Maggie concentrated on cutting up her pancakes with her fork, reluctant to disclose the extent of her stupidity. 'Looking for my dog,' she mumbled.

'This grows more interesting by the minute,' he said sarcastically. 'How did you lose your dog?'

'When I let him out of the car to . . . to do his business, he ran off. I . . . I was worried about him.' She sloshed the syrup around in her plate before venturing to ask, 'How did you happen to find me? The last thing I remember is getting stuck under a big rock and thinking I'd rest awhile.'

He snorted. 'The dog was smarter than you. He found me. At first I thought he was lost, but he wouldn't come in and seemed pretty insistent that I came out. I finally did, and he led me straight to you. Just in time, too,' he added soberly. 'You were well on your way to a bad case of hypothermia. If my phone hadn't gone wrong, I would have called for an ambulance. As it was, I had to do the best I could on my own.'

'Hypothermia?' she asked uncertainly. 'I'm not sure I know what that is.'

'Exposure is what most people call it. Your body was losing heat at a faster rate than it could produce it. Your clothes were sopping wet. You shouldn't ski in jeans. Denim loses heat so quickly when it's wet you might as well be nude.'

Maggie could feel the heat rushing to colour her

cheeks. She had been nude.

He ignored her blush. 'By the time I found you, you were already incoherent, hallucinating and barely able to stand.' He gave her a questioning look. 'You thought I was someone named Bayard.'

'My brother. I was meeting him in Aspen.' She couldn't look at him. 'And does treatment for hypothermia normally include having sexual relations with the victim?'

'No,' he said coldly. 'And neither did your treatment.'

Her relief was overwhelming. If she could believe him. 'I suppose,' she went on quickly, before she lost her nerve, 'you have a good explanation for the fact that when I woke up this morning you were in my bed and we were both naked.'

'You were in my bed,' he pointed out.

That brought her head up. 'Are you saying that I crawled into bed with *you*?'

He slammed his coffee-mug down on the table. 'Listen, Red. I've had about all I'm going to take from you. In case it hasn't got through your thick skull yet, I saved your life last night. I am not some dirty sex-fiend who gets his kicks out of taking advantage of an unconscious woman. It just so happens that the best way to warm up a severely chilled body, which I'd like to assure you you certainly had last night, is by warming the person as fast as possible. I don't have any heating pads or electric blankets here, so the only solution was to remove both our clothes and huddle together hoping that my body heat was enough to warm you up.' He was shouting by now. 'You think I enjoyed hugging an icicle to my bare skin?'

'If that's true, then why did you kiss me this

morning?'

He grinned wryly at her. 'Because when I woke up this morning I wasn't hugging an icicle any more. Instead I discovered an armful of warm, throbbing flesh topped by flaming red hair.'

'Oh.' The kitchen felt unbearably warm.

'I don't believe I've ever seen a person who blushes as much as you do.'

'It's a red-headed curse,' she said crossly. 'Along with having to stay out of the sun, everyone expecting you to have a temper and having nicknames like Carrot-top and Red. I've always wanted to be a blonde.'

He shook his head. 'I can't see you as a blonde.'

'Why not? Because I don't look like the type that can have more fun?' she asked indignantly.

'I'm beginning to believe one part of the myth.'

She looked at him suspiciously. His face was perfectly sober but laughter lurked in the depths of his blue eyes. 'I'm going to hate myself for asking, but . . .?'

'That red-heads have a hair-trigger temper,' he said deliberately.

Maggie put her elbows on the table and rested her chin on her hands. Widening her eyes at him, she asked with spurious interest. 'Did you have to pay the magazine?'

He frowned at her. 'I don't know what you mean.'

'To dub you one of the most eligible batchelors, et cetera, et cetera. I don't see it myself. You must be very rich to make up for your unpleasant personality.'

To her annoyance, the remark amused him instead of irritating him as she had intended. 'Depends upon how rich you want. I don't run to yachts and castles in Spain, but I can handle a diamond now and again.'

'Paltry.' She waved away his meagre fortune. 'I particularly wanted a castle in Spain.'

'Sorry. You landed on the wrong doorstep for that.'

'Oh, I don't know,' she said airily. 'There's always a spot of blackmail.'

'Meaning?'

'Who knows how much it would be worth to you for me to keep quiet about our activities this morning?'

'Sorry to disappoint you. No wife. No jealous lover.'

'I was thinking more along the lines of newspapers.' She leaned back and spread her arms wide. 'You gave me the idea when you accused me of being a newspaper reporter. I can see it now. Two-inch leadlines. "I woke up in bed with Colorado's most eligible batchelor!" ' She bestowed upon him a smile of wicked triumph.

He considered her remark before adding thoughtfully. 'Personally, I prefer, "Librarian slips between the covers".'

'How about, "The naked truth about Colorado's most eligible bachelor!"?'

' "Librarian open book to me, he says".'

She grimaced. 'That's really awful. How about "Bachelor shelves clothes for librarian"?'

' "More than her hair was red".'

' "Bachelor bares body to . . ." See. It would be better if I were blonde.'

' "Bachelor bares body to buxom blonde', you mean?'

Maggie could feel the incriminating flush as she

thought of her slender shape. If there was one thing that she was not, it was buxom. Maybe he really hadn't noticed much about her naked body in his preoccupation with warming it up. The look in his eyes disabused her of that notion. Not only did he know the exact dimensions of her body, he was well aware of what thoughts were going through her mind at that very moment. She sought to divert his thoughts. 'I have not thanked you yet for saving my life,' she said primly. 'It was very kind of you, Mr . . . Oh, this is ridiculous. What is your name, anyway?' she asked crossly. 'I can't go around calling you Mr Peters when I know very well that's not your name.'

'Call me Nick.' Correctly interpreting the negative shake of her head, he added firmly, 'That is my name.'

She noticed he didn't insist that Peters was his last name. 'All right,' she conceded. 'We'll just be Nick and Maggie.'

CHAPTER TWO

AS SHE helped him clean up the kitchen he asked her more about herself. Maggie told him about how her parents had been driving home one evening when a drunken driver side-swiped their car killing them both, while he had suffered no more than a broken arm. Her grandmother had come to live with the three children, since Maggie, the eldest, was only in high school at the time. She mentioned that her grandmother had recently died, glossing over Nana's long illness, the struggles to care for her grandmother at home aided by visiting nurses, the fear that Nana would die and the courts would put Julie into a foster home, and the relief when Nana had hung on through sheer will and determination until only a few months before Julie's eighteenth birthday.

Maggie couldn't remember when life hadn't been a struggle. As a teacher, her father hadn't been able to save much before his death and Nana's meagre savings had been depleted by her long illness. Luckily insurance had taken care of the small house where they were living, but even so Maggie had waited at tables, walked dogs, typed term papers, baby-sat and done any other odd chore that came her way. By scrimping, saving and making every penny go twice as far as could be humanly expected, she had managed to put herself through the university.

She hadn't been the only member of the family called upon to sacrifice. Until her illness, Nana had been a tremendous help, stretching the food budget to delicious and incredible lengths. Even as youngsters, Bayard and Julie had worked for every penny of their spending money and done their share to help around the house and to care for their beloved Nana. They seldom grumbled, but Maggie knew that Bayard had hated working in the kitchen of a fraternity house to pay the school fees not covered by his scholarships, and that Julie longed for shop-bought clothes in place of those sewn by Maggie. Their uncomplaining acceptance of the spartan regime forced on them by circumstances had torn at Maggie's heart when she had seen the free-spending ways of their friends, and she had done her best to shelter them from the harshest realities of life by not showing them the bills for Nana's care and by hiding her fears that they would have to mortgage their home and risk losing it.

'You didn't say whereabouts in Arizona you live,' Nick said.

'I'll dry than pan.' Maggie reached over and rescued the skillet that was dripping all over the floor. It hadn't escaped her attention that Nick had volunteered very little information about himself. Two could play his wary game, and she had been careful to omit details like her last name and the fact that she lived in Tucson. She would trust him only as far as he trusted her. Before he could repeat his question, she hastily changed the subject. 'If you dislike the idea of being labelled an eligible bachelor so much, why did you agree to the article?'

'Who said anything about agreeing? The magazine didn't bother to ask me. They selected ten guys and then wrote a bunch of claptrap about us based on newspaper files, gossip and pure conjecture. Mostly the latter, as far as I was concerned.'

'Can't you sue or something?' She hung up the damp towel as he put away the last of the dishes.

'They didn't exactly slander me or publish lies. What they did was ferret out many of my personal habits and broadcast them to the world. The article made it very clear that none of the subjects had co-operated with the author and that all that stuff about my searching for a wife was strictly opinion. Unfortunately,' he added drily, 'an opinion that most of the single young women in Colorado want to believe, or so it seems to me.'

'Quite an ego-trip,' Maggie remarked in a light voice, following him into the living-room.

He gave her an odd look. 'On the contrary. It's rather deflating to realise the number of women who view me as nothing more than a meal-ticket.'

'Rather hard on the opposite sex, aren't you?'

'You think so? I've had two women trip at my feet, one pretend that she thought my car was hers, and a flood of job applications at the shop, and my neighbours are outraged by the number of women slowly driving by, not to mention the thousands who walk their dogs down our street. I'm harassed when I go to the movies; I have to shop by phone and my favourite restaurant is so booked by single women these days I can't even get a table. My entire life has been invaded by women with one goal in mind—to be Mrs Nicholas . . . um . . . Peters.'

Maggie gave him a quizzical look as he stumbled over the last name. 'Well, this is your lucky day,' she said. 'Maggie Peters doesn't have the cachet that I want with my married name.'

'I find it hard to believe that your sole prerequisite for a husband is the right-sounding name.'

'Since you seem to be the expert on the subject, tell me what I should be looking for,' she invited.

Leaning back against the sofa he gave serious attention to her frivolous remark. 'If I were a woman, first off, I'd want a man who would treat me right. All the money in the world wouldn't make up for a man who beat his wife or treated her with contempt. I'd want a man who'd laugh with me, converse with me, respect my opinions. A friend and companion. Someone to grow happily old with.'

'What about love?'

He shrugged. 'Love is an ephemeral emotion. If it's part of the whole package, OK, but friendship and respect are more substantial. You can count on them.'

The depth of feeling in his voice startled Maggie, and she tried for a lighter touch. 'Little did I realise that I was snowed in with an advice-to-the-lovelorn columnist.'

He grinned at her. 'I can't imagine a woman like you ever needing that kind of help. You must have a hundred men on the string.'

Maggie swallowed a grin at the outrageous flattery. 'Just Archie. My one and only love.'

'Tell me more about this Archie character. What does he do for a living?'

'As little as possible. In fact,' she confided, 'I support him. Archie lives with me.'

At the sound of his name, Archie raised his head and barked sharply before subsiding back to the floor. Nick grinned. 'C'mere, Archie.'

'Traitor,' Maggie said to the setter as he obediently padded over to where Nick sat on the sofa and laid his red head against his knee.

Nick smoothed the setter's red hair. 'You two make quite a pair. I've heard that dogs often resemble their owners.'

'Are you saying I have a long nose?'

'Are you telling me that the red hair is a coincidence?' he countered.

'No,' she admitted. 'Nana, my grandmother, gave Archie to me for Christmas the year I was sixteen. She was cursed with red hair, too, and she knew how much I hated mine. Archie was her way of trying to convince me that red hair wasn't so bad.'

'She sounds like a nice lady.'

'Yes. I miss her a lot. It's been six months, but still . . .' Her voice died away. Nana's suffering near the end had been so intense that Maggie's grief had been eased by the knowledge that at least Nana wasn't in pain any more. At the same time, Nana had been the one who had shared with Maggie the burdens of caring for the children, and had buoyed her up with love and astringent advice. Just as Maggie was the foundation on which Julie and Bayard depended, so had Nana been the rock that Maggie leaned upon.

'So there's just you and the two little kids,' Nick said. 'I don't understand how you confused me with your little brother when I found you.'

'The truth is,' Maggie said slowly, 'Bayard is only seventeen months younger than me. I have a tendency to forget that. Which is what probably started the fight that caused this whole mess.'

'Fight?'

Maggie walked over to the window and looked out into a world that was totally white. 'Bayard and Julie, she's eighteen, accused me of being too bossy. We had a big fight about it.' With Bayard possessing his share of the Russell temper, arguments between the two of them were not so unusual. Only this time, Julie, normally a non-participant in their raging battles, had devastated Maggie by siding with her brother. 'They were still angry with me when they left.'

'Even so, they'll be worried when you don't show up in Aspen. I wish the phone were working.' He joined her at the window. 'No telling when this is going to clear up so that you can leave.' A whirling dervish of white substantiated his observation.

Maggie shook her head. 'Only Bayard is in Aspen. Julie went with a schoolfriend and her parents to California for a week. As for Bayard, he's not exactly expecting me.' She caught his knowing look out of the corner of her eye. 'It's not what you're thinking. Bayard invited me to join him and his friends.'

'Why didn't you go with them?'

'It was one of those silly little things. Bayard and Julie had been saying that our house looked shabby compared to their friends' homes. So, intending to surprise them, I bought wallpaper and paint, thinking that we could fix up the house over the holidays. Only the surprise was on me. They had both come home that night all excited and anxious to tell me about their plans. I was hurt that they wanted to spend the holidays separately instead of as a family, and disappointed that they viewed my idea as just another chore. Bayard tried to persuade me to go skiing, but I got on my high horse and insisted that someone had to stay home to do the work.'

'I'm beginning to understand your earlier reference to the Little Red Hen,' Nick said.

'Yes. I was going to show them. I would do it all

by myself, making them suffer horrible pangs of guilt. Bayard was so miffed with me when he left, he'd never call me to see how I was for fear I'd still be playing the martyr.'

'So how did it happen that you were headed for Aspen?'

'I started to paint the kitchen. Feeling pretty darn sorry for myself, I might add. With each stroke of the brush, I'd enumerate another reason why Bayard should be nicer or Julie more appreciative, and suddenly I saw myself as they must see me. A nag, a spoil-sport, a party-pooper. Oh yes, they'd called me all those things. And they were right. I shouldn't have made plans for them without consulting them. If redoing the house was to be a family project, they had a right to help select the paint and paper. The kitchen didn't have to be painted this particular week. It's needed new paint for years. Another week wouldn't hurt.'

'Is that what made you come to your senses and decided to wait until you had help instead of doing all the work yourself?'

'It was more than that. Bayard and Julie accused me of forgetting what it was like to be young, to enjoy life.' With her finger she outlined the lacy frost patterns on the cold window. 'I saw myself growing old and discovering that I'd never really lived.'

'So you finished painting the kitchen and decided to drive to Aspen.'

'Not exactly. The second I made my decision, I popped the lid back on the paint, packed my suitcase, borrowed some skis and drove away.' She blushed. 'I didn't even stop to clean the brush. I just tossed it in the bin,'

Nick threw back his head and roared with laughter

at her confession. 'When you kick over the traces, you go all the way, don't you?' he teased. 'What you really are saying is that you ran away from home. And look what happened. Here you are, stuck in the woods with a perfect stranger and no one even knows you are missing.'

She looked at him in dismay. That was exactly what she had said. Trying to hide the panicky feeling that crawled around inside her stomach, she walked casually away from the window. Just because this man was tall, good-looking and blessed with an abundance of charm didn't mean that he couldn't be some sexual pervert or mass murderer. Weren't they usually known for their charm? After all, what did she know about hypothermia? She only had his word for it that removing her clothes had been necessary for her survival. Who knew what ungodly things he had done to her body while she was unconscious? And naked. Crossing her arms in front of her chest, she shivered.

'Cold? I can turn up the furnace. The fireplace is only for show when it's this cold, I'm afraid. More heat goes up the chimney than heats the living-room.'

'No, no. I'm fine, really,' she said, moving across the room towards the kitchen. Next he would suggest that they huddle together in bed. He grinned at her retreat. Why had his smile seemed so attractive a few minutes ago when it looked positively fiendish now?

'This storm doesn't look like letting up for some time. It's going to get pretty uncomfortable around here if you persist in thinking I'm going to slit your throat or ravage your body.'

'What ever gave you the idea I thought that?' Maggie asked. She blinked her eyes in despair. Even a madman would be able to read the fear in her high-pitched voice.

'It's pretty obvious. Luckily for you, I only murder two women a month, and I've already filled my quota for December.'

Maggie eyed him warily. 'If it's such a far-fetched idea, how come you immediately knew that was what I was thinking?'

'That look of panic on your face was my first clue. The second was when you suddenly edged away from me. As for the third,' he sighed loudly. 'No, you have the wrong drawer. The butcher-knives are in the left one.'

Maggie snatched back her hand as if she had been burned. She thought she had been so subtle in her movements. In front of the fireplace Archie sat up. Perhaps there was an undercurrent of emotion that alerted him. Perhaps he sensed Maggie's fears. At any rate, he sprang to his feet and growled softly. Then walking over to Nick, Archie thrust his muzzle into Nick's hand. 'He wants to go out,' Maggie said shakily. For a moment there . . .

Nick reached down and scratched the large setter behind his floppy ears, all the while eyeing Maggie quizzically. 'At least Archie trusts me. He looks like a pretty good watchdog to me.'

'Which proves you know absolutely nothing about dogs. Archie would hand the key to the safe to any burglar who would scratch behind his ears.' She paused. 'Maybe you do know something about dogs,' she added slowly.

'Now why do I think that discovery is another black mark against me? Most people consider a fondness for dogs is a positive trait.' Following Archie to the door, he attached him to a long rope before letting him out.

A frigid blast of air rushed into the room and swirled about Maggie's ankles. He was right about one thing. Whoever, whatever he was, until the storm had exhausted its fury, she was fated to remain here with him in this cabin. She took a deep breath. 'You never told me what you do when you're not escaping from hordes of women.'

He raised a sarcastic brow. 'Decided that I'm not a mass murderer after all?'

'I'll give you the benefit of the doubt,' she said bravely. 'After all, you are right that we are stuck here together. We may as well make the most of it.' As his lips twitched, she realised how her statement could be misconstrued, and she rushed to continue, 'I meant, be nice to each other . . .' Her voice trailed off at the wicked, teasing look on his face.

'Exactly how nice did you have in mind?' he asked.

'I meant be polite and you know it,' she said sharply.

'Better watch it, Red,' he advised. 'Your red hair is showing again.'

'My red hair is always showing,' Maggie snapped. 'Apparently, your arrogance and rudeness are as hard to hide as my red hair is.'

He gave her a look of approval. 'You're a fighter; I like that. People who go to pieces in a crisis leave me cold. I'd hate to be snowed in with some ninny who spent the whole time snivelling with fear or demanding that I *do* something to get her back to civilisation. I appreciate your sensible acceptance of circumstances.'

'If I were sensible, I wouldn't be here,' Maggie said, her voice tinged with the bitter awareness that her present predicament was entirely of her own making.

Nick uttered a short laugh. 'There's something in that,' he conceded. Responding to a noise at the door, he grabbed a towel from the kitchen and then opened the door for Archie. Once again the whirling snow and wind shrieked and screamed in an effort to gain entry to the warm cabin. Nick grabbed Archie's collar with one hand while thrusting the door closed with his hip. Then he briskly towelled the dog dry.

It was obvious to Maggie that Archie had no reservations about Nick. The dog stood patiently as the man rubbed his long-haired coat to a dull gleam. 'Archie likes you,' she said begrudgingly. 'Of course, Irish setters are notoriously stupid.'

'Notoriously,' Nick agreed, a glint in his eye. 'I've been told that it's the flame-red hair. Burns up their brains. What do you think?'

'I think that if anyone gets murdered in this cabin before the storm lets up, it's likely to be you.'

Nick reached out his hand. 'What do you say we call a ceasefire?'

Slowly Maggie put her hand in his. 'All right, Truce.'

'Just for the duration, of course,' Nick added smoothly.

'What does that mean?'

'As soon as the weather clears up, I'm free to strangle you, or slit your throat, or do whatever ghoulish thing it is that I do to my victims.'

Maggie refused to be further intimidated. 'It's a deal. Of course, it works both ways. I'm free to ensnare you in my matrimonial trap.'

Nick still held her hand. 'You're free to try,' he said softly, tugging her closer to him.

Her resistance was minimal. Only because she

didn't want to upset their fragile truce, she told herself. And because she was just the tiniest bit curious. Had his kisses this morning been as fantastic as she remembered, or was that only part of a dream?

He tasted of syrup and coffee. Maggie wondered if all morning kisses had such a domestic flavour. This was new and unfamiliar territory to her. While other young girls had been giggling over dances and experimenting with make-up and confiding girlish secrets to each other, Maggie had been staggering under the burdens of parenthood. Any boy who was attracted to the skinny, freckled, red-haired young woman quickly lost interest when he realised that Maggie's responsibilities allowed no time for dalliance. As her brother and sister had grown older and she might have expected to have more time to herself, there had been Nana's unexpected illness. As a consequence, even though she was twenty-four years old, Maggie was as innocent as a young girl when it came to impassioned kisses, fumbling under loosened clothing or the touch of a man's hand against her bare skin. Perhaps sensing that innocence, Nick held her loosely within his embrace. His tacit assurance that she could break off the kiss at any time she chose gave her courage and she eagerly explored the depths of his mouth.

Only when Nick guided her on to the sofa, his hands warm under the sweater against her skin, did she realise where her experimenting was leading to. Abruptly she leaned away, her mouth still tasting the sweetness of his. 'I'm . . . I'm . . . sorry,' she stammered, stunned by her own audacity.

Nick's fingers traced lazy circles along either side of her spine. 'Why?'

'Why?' she asked wildly. 'If we're doing that after

breakfast, what will we be doing after dinner?'

He leaned down and nipped her ear lobe. 'More of the same if you intend to try and ensare me in your coils,' he said, his warm, moist breath eddying into her ear.

Maggie shuddered and jerked away. 'Don't. That's as bad as Archie licking the inside of my ear to wake me up. It gives me goose bumps.' She rapidly rubbed her arms to chase away the chills.

Nick looked at her through narrowed eyes before removing his hands from her sweater and pulling it back down around her hips. 'I can't decide if you're for real or not. One minute you're a total innocent, the next you're a steaming inferno, and then suddenly you're a gauche teenager. Which is the real Maggie?'

She shrugged. 'All of them, I guess.' Edging away from him on the sofa, she added, 'No doubt you're used to much more sophisticated women.'

'No doubt. Kissing a librarian is a new experience for me. You don't exactly fit the image of an old spinster with a stern finger against her lips.' He laughed, a low amused chuckle that caused strange happenings in the pit of Maggie's stomach. 'Just as well. Those lips aren't meant for hiding behind a finger.'

She tossed her hair, ignoring his last remark. 'You haven't been in a library for a long time if you think that all librarians do is run around telling everyone to be quiet.'

He grabbed a stray red curl, and concentrating on wrapping it aroundd his finger, he said, 'My mistake. I didn't know what I was missing.' His hand tightened on her hair, tugging her head closer to his lips.

By the time he released her Maggie was trembling,

her traitorous body aching to melt against his. With supreme effort, she brought her tangled emotions under some kind of control. 'What happened to our truce?' she asked, her voice barely wavering.

He raised an enquiring eyebrow. 'I wasn't aware anything had happened to it.'

'You broke it when you kissed me.'

'There was nothing said about not kissing you. I just promised not to murder you.'

'You promised not to do anything ghoulish,' Maggie said.

Nick regarded her thoughtfully. 'I hope the storm lasts for quite a while. I think I'm going to need a long time to make up my mind.' He stood up and walked across the room. 'I have a stack of paperwork to do. There's plenty of reading material in the bookcase, if you're interested.' Snapping open a stuffed leather briefcase, he picked up a ballpoint pen and began shuffling through the papers.

Silence reigned for about five minutes broken only by the clicking of Nick's pen. Maggie mulled over his enigmatic remark until her curiosity got the better of her. 'Make up your mind about what?' she demanded.

Nick frowned at her, his thoughts clearly on the papers in front of him. 'What?'

'You said you needed a long time to make up your mind. About what?'

One corner of his mouth twitched. 'I wondered how long it would take before you asked.'

'Well?'

'The method.' He leaned back, studying her with cool blue eyes as he tapped the pen against his lower lip. 'The method for disposing of an ill-mannered, ungrateful, carrot-topped librarian.'

'Dis . . . disposing?'

'Murder most foul,' he hissed dramatically.

'You're kidding,' she said uneasily.

'Am I?'

She would not let her imagination override her better judgement. Of course he was teasing her, Maggie assured herself stoutly as she browsed through the surprisingly eclectic and up-to-date collection of books. Finding an old favourite, she curled up in an enormous chair in the corner. Today, however, the antics and repartee of the heroine failed to capture her interest. Her attention kept straying to the man of mystery across the room. His steadfast refusal to disclose his surname indicated a man with something to hide, but she was aware that only his prompt recognition of her plight along with his swift and efficient treatment had saved her life last night. All too vivid were memories of the cold, her over-whelming urge to sleep, the hallucinations.

She covertly studied him as he concentrated on his papers. Dressed in a red tartan wool shirt buttoned over a solid red turtleneck jersey that enhanced his darkly handsome appearance, he looked too danger-ous to be actually dangerous, she decided. His hair was mussed from running his fingers through it and he had rolled his shirt cuffs up to his elbows. The tip of his tongue stuck out at the corner of his mouth as he scowled in exasperation at the paper before him. Maggie was reminded of Bayard when he was work-ing on a particularly difficult problem in mathematics.

He didn't look like a high-powered executive, either. And what made her think he was? He had never said so. In fact, he had said remarkably little about himself. A sudden thought amused her. If he really was deemed one of Colorado's most eligible bachelors, some women might consider being snowbound with him a very enviable position in which to find oneself. Of course, they probably wouldn't be impressed by the fact that he was totally oblivious of her presence. Playing second fiddle to a bunch of papers. That ought to convince her, if nothing else did, that whatever he was he wasn't a sex maniac. Or a mass murderer. He was merely teasing her. That was the curse of being addicted to reading mystery novels. A person began to inject sinister meaning into the most innocent activity.

She had better stop staring at him. She had read once that the Indians believed if you stared directly at someone long enough that person could feel your eyes. The last thing she wanted was to be caught in the act of watching him.

She looked around the large cabin. Huge overhead beams, smooth log walls, a massive stone fireplace, plenty of large chairs and an enormous sofa—all with an air of comfortable rusticity. Archie was a large splash of reddish-orange on the deep brown ocean of thick carpet. Over the fireplace hung an enormous painting of a russet-coloured dog gazing longingly upwards at a V-shaped flight of geese. The dog could have been Archie's double. Maggie moved closer to inspect the painting.

'That's Casey. He and my grandfather were the best bird-hunters in the area. According to Grandad, that is.' Nick stretched and rubbed the back of his neck.

'Do you hunt?'

'No, I've never cared for it. I prefer fishing. It, and this cabin, are my escape valves from the outside world.'

'Escape. What a lovely-sounding word. If you only knew how many times I've longed to escape from my humdrum existence.'

'To a castle in Spain?' he asked lightly.

'Or a bungalow in Bermuda, the Ritz in Paris in the spring, a tropical island . . . Since escape of any kind is impossible, why not dream of somewhere terribly exotic? Do you know, this is the first time I've been this far from Tu . . . ah . . . home in years. It must be nice to be able to get away from the rest of the world,' she added wistfully.

'Nice, but almost impossible.'

'I suppose that's a reminder that I'm intruding?' Maggie flared.

He laughed. 'Not at all. I simply meant that my responsibilities seldom allow me to get away. As a matter of fact, you're restful to have around.'

His choice of labels stung. She doubted that he normally selected his female companions based on their ability to bore. 'How do you manage to escape up here without hordes of matrimonially-minded women in hot pursuit?' she asked pointedly.

'You're determined to make me out a pompous ass because I jumped to a conclusion about how you happened to show up here, aren't you?' he asked wryly.

'*I* can't make you a pompous ass,' she returned swiftly. 'You are the one who claims that pursuing women have imprisoned you in your home.'

'I don't think I quite made that claim. However, to answer your initial question about the cabin, luckily the magazine failed to discover its existence. The family has a big place up near Estes Park—has for years—and I still go up there occasionally, but I pretty much turned it over to my sister when I bought this place a couple of years ago. Only a very small circle of friends know about it. Believe it or not, you're the first woman who's ever been here, outside of family.'

'How about the woman who owns these?' Maggie tugged at the jeans she was wearing.

'They belong to my sister. She forgot them when she was up with her husband last month.'

'Tell me more about your family. You were obviously born with a silver spoon in your mouth.'

'Don't be so stingy. An entire silver service for twelve.'

'Oh, I see. Your last name must be Rockerfeller, or Morgan, or Vanderbilt or . . .?'

The amused glint in his eye acknowledged her subtle probe for information. 'As a matter of fact, my great-great-grandfather was a dirt-poor immigrant with a wife and baby when he heard "gold" and headed west to make his fortune.'

'Obviously he made it.'

'Not in the gold fields. Searching for a strike was back-breaking labour and an enormous gamble. He soon realised that his wife was making more money back in town baking bread and cutting hair than he was out in countryside. He moved back to town and started a little general store, grubstaking the miners in exchange for a share of their profits. A wise and profitable decision for which I am deeply grateful.'

'You inherited your money?'

'You needn't sound so disapproving. As a matter of fact, I inherited a business. When my dad had to retire early for health reasons, I took over.'

'It's always nice to start at the top,' she mocked.

He grinned. 'Not exactly at the top. Dad groomed me to run the business ever since I was a young boy. I don't think there was any part of the store where I didn't work at one time or the other. I started out as a janitor. I was furious. I wanted to sell toys.' His grin broadened. 'I was seven years old and Dad paid me twenty-five cents an hour. He said that's how he started. Grandad was still alive then and I can remember his chiming in that Dad had been overpaid at that.'

She laughed with him before pointing out, 'Even if you did start at the bottom, so to speak, you always knew that the store would some day be yours. You must have always felt . . . oh, I don't know . . . provided for.'

'You overrate the value of money.'

'Easy sentiments for a man who's just admitted that he's never been in need.'

'What would you buy if you had all the money you wanted?' he asked curiously, his hands clasped behind his head, his legs stretched out in front of him.

'That's easy,' she answered. 'For Julie, all the designer jeans she could ever want, and party dresses, and letting her get her hair cut at an expensive salon instead of at the chain down at the mall. For Bayard, a sports car instead of the jalopy he nurses along year after year. For me, new furniture and wallpaper that wasn't on sale. I could give to charities that I believed in without worrying if I was depriving the kids of something they needed.' She smiled ruefully. 'It sounds like I've spent a lot of time thinking about it, but I really haven't. The possibility of our ever coming into money is so remote . . . although sometimes I have to admit I feel as if I'd do anything for money.'

'Don't tell me that you're naïve enough to believe

that money can buy happiness.'

'No, not really. But, at least, with money I'd have a whole different set of problems. I could have paid someone else to come in and paint and wallpaper, setting me free to run off to Aspen with Bayard.'

'You did run off to Aspen,' he reminded her.

'True, and look at the mess I landed in. "Just deserts," as my grandmother would have said.'

'I'm not sure that I like being compared to an ice-cream sundae,' Nick said facetiously.

'Not even chocolate with gobs of whipped cream and a cherry on top?'

'Well,' Nick drawled, 'I guess if you add a cherry.'

Maggie's heart took an alarming dip. Nick's ability to laugh at himself was as disarming as the whimsical smile on his face. Buffeted by a barrage of unfamiliar emotions she looked out of the window. Gusts of wind battered the panes of glass while a screen of white hid the landscape from view. 'When will it ever stop?'

Nick shrugged. 'Hard to say. I'm not complaining. A snug little cabin, plenty of food and a beautiful red-head to keep me warm. What more could a man want?' He eyed her with interest before adding in a voice tinged with amusement, 'You're blushing again.'

Fortunately for Maggie's rattled composure, Archie provided a welcome interruption by demanding to go outside.

CHAPTER THREE

BY LUNCH TIME Maggie had her emotions under
control again. No doubt Nick was one of those men
to whom flirting was as natural as breathing. She had
been a fool to take any of his provocative remarks
seriously. Over sandwiches she managed to guide the
conversation back to his family and was treated to
tales of the ancestor fresh off the boat from
Tipperary who had heard about the discovery of gold
in Colorado and immediately travelled west. The
family business had grown and flourished with each
son following in his father's footsteps.

'So you can see that I grew up with the business,'
Nick was saying. 'Our name has long stood for
something out here. I could rest on its laurels, but
complacency would soon put us out of business. My
great-great-grandad didn't work his legs off making a
success of his store for some lazy descendant to allow
it to fail. There's a lot of competition for each
customer today. It's up to me to make sure that he or
she wants to shop at our store. That's the challenge.
To keep growing, to pick up the new customer
without losing the old.' He grinned wryly at Maggie.
'You shouldn't let me get started on my sales-pitch to
new personnel. I'll bore the socks off you.'

'I wasn't bored,' Maggied denied in all honesty.
She was fascinated by Nick's revealing conversation.
One could almost say that his life had been as
dedicated to and defined by responsibility as hers
had. On a different level, to be sure, but the

similarity was inescapable.

Following lunch Nick returned to his paperwork, leaving Maggie to entertain herself. Retrieving her book, she wandered into the bedroom, and propping pillows up on the bed, lay down to read. It wasn't long, however, before once again her thoughts wandered from the printed page.

It seemed as if from the moment of birth she had been Maggie the dependable one, Maggie the steady one, Maggie the . . . the boring one. Anyone who knew her would be quick to say that Maggie never took risks, never did the unexpected. For the first time in her life she had acted totally on impulse, and as a result had barely avoided tragedy. What would Julie and Bayard have done if Nick hadn't found her? How could they have managed? She had been stupid and irresponsible, her actions rash and ill-judged.

And look what had happened. Here she was in the middle of a raging blizzard, in a cabin out in the middle of the woods, Heaven only knew where, with a strange man, and—and it was exhilarating. For the first time in her life she was having an adventure. Maggie Russell, dull-as-dishwater librarian, was living life instead of reading about it.

The neglected book dropped unheeded to the bed, and she sat up. He had called her beautiful. A mirror across the room reflected her image back to her. Pale skin with cheeks that were blotches of colour. The nose was nicely shaped. But beautiful? Not with all those freckles that no amount of lemon juice could efface.

And then there was her hair. Many times her mother and Julie had tactfully suggested that perhaps if she cut it short it would be less noticeable, but on this point Maggie had been perversely stubborn. Her grandmother had red hair—it was the McPherson blood, she often said proudly, and so Maggie pretended that she really didn't mind her flaming red locks. As a child she had learned to endure the fact that people seemed to have an uncontrollable urge to pat red-haired children on the head. No one ever patted Julie's head. When they looked at Maggie's younger sister they always said, 'What a lovely child.' When they looked at Maggie they said, 'Your mother says you're a big help to her.' She had recognised that in their kind way they were saying that she'd never be pretty, so she had better grow up to be a hard-worker.

Maggie slowly untied the shoelace at the nape of her neck, freeing her mane of hair. Long ago she had given up trying to straighten the wild curls, and it encircled her head now in a fiery cloud. With slow, languorous movements she half turned away and fluffed up her hair before gazing back over her shoulder at the mirror in what she hoped was a sultry manner.

The pose made her grin. If only her friends and students could see her now. The prim Miss Russell without bun and horn-rimmed glasses. There was a certain amount of fun and flattery to be derived from the notion that the most attractive man she had ever met thought that she was a red-headed adventurer. Her eyelids drooped lower as she lost herself in her fantasies. Margaret Russell, red-headed bombshell taking society by storm, her goal to trap suave man-about-town Nick Peters in marriage. Lt Maggie Russell, NYPD, working undercover to expose underworld crime czar Nick Peters. Magda Russellovitch, Russian spy, trying to persuade

CIA henchman Nick Peters to divulge the secret plan to her.

'Do you plan to sleep all the afternoon?'

'I won't sleep with you,' she said sleepily, 'not until you tell me where they are.'

'That's too good a deal to pass up.' Nick's mouth hovered above hers. 'What is "they"?'

Maggie pouted in disappointment. What kind of secret agent was he if he didn't even know that he was supposed to try to persuade her? 'You know.'

That was better. Much better. Warm lips, firm pressure persuading hers to part, skilful domination of her mouth. A hand under her sweater, warm against her skin. Her eyes popped open. 'I . . . I must have been dreaming,' she said wildly.

Nick's fingers combed through the long, curly strands of her hair. 'Of the Prince waking Sleeping Beauty?'

'Uh—not exactly.'

He cocked an inquisitive brow.

'I was dreaming that . . . that you . . . you were a secret agent,' she finished in a rush.

He threw back his head and laughed. It was a wonderful laugh, so carefree and uninhibited. Everything that she was not. He was sitting on the bed beside her, one arm on either side of her body fencing her in. She should have felt threatened, but she didn't. Instead, she felt—reckless. Slowly, wary of rejection, or even worse, ridicule, she reached up and traced the cleft of his chin with a shaking finger. The laughter in his eyes died away to be replaced with another, more subtle emotion—one that Maggie couldn't decipher. He sat very still, his gaze intent on her face.

Avoiding his eyes, she concentrated on the path

her finger was following. Up the cleft, the few bristles that he had missed in shaving were scratchy against her finger. His lips were smooth in contrast. He opened his mouth and sucked deliberately on her finger. Deep within her she began to ache with unfamiliar pressures and she turned her head and rubbed her cheek against the wool-clad arm nearest to her as if that would ease the ache. The palm of her hand was warm where it rested against his face, and his teeth rasped against the skin of her finger as he nibbled on the tip. A delicate action, and at the same time unbelievably erotic. The ache within her grew deeper. He abandoned the moistened finger for her lips. Lips that opened at his persuasive touch. His mouth exploring hers, he pushed her over, making room for his body on the bed, and lay down, his long length half covering her body, his legs entwined with hers. As she surrendered to the mastery of his mouth and hands, she realised that something wonderful had been missing from her life all these years.

Sighing, Nick lifted his head from hers and tugged her sweater down over swollen breasts. 'When I came in here to waken you, that wasn't quite what I had in mind,' he said huskily.

Maggie opened her eyes and then quickly closed them against the dancing flames from the half-hooded eyes staring down at her. Her body was still flushed with the heat of desire and, turning from his study of her, she buried her head in the curve of his shoulder. The tangy aroma of his aftershave lingered on his skin and teased at her nostrils. Pressing her aching breasts against his chest offered some small measure of consolation for the loss of the magical fingers which had exacted moans of longing from her. She ought to be shamed by the memory of the way she had abandoned all restraint and had eagerly followed Nick's lead down unfamiliar paths and byways. Maybe she ought to be, but she wasn't. Not by a long way. Even if she died an old maid she would have the memories of these kisses to sustain her. The day that Maggie Russell had let her hair down.

'What's that little smile of satisfaction for?' Nick had risen up on one elbow and was watching her.

'Sheer enjoyment. That's the nicest wake-up call I've ever had.' Her body and emotions were more under control now, and she stretched ostentatiously, in the process breaking the contact between their bodies.

The knowing look on his face told her that he recognised her retreat. 'For some reason, I was expecting to have my face slapped.' Grabbing one of the pillows that had been pushed to the side, he folded it in half and tucked it behind her head, doing the same with another for himself.

'Is that usually what happens to you?' she asked daringly.

'No, but then, I've never kissed a librarian before.'

'Is that why you stopped?'

'I stopped because I didn't want things to get out of hand. And,' he paused, staring thoughtfully at their twin images in the mirror across the room, 'no matter how enthusiastic a participant you were, I had the oddest impression that I was the teacher and you were my student.'

'That's probably because you're so much older than me,' Maggie said waspishly. He couldn't be a very polished seducer if he didn't know that a woman didn't like her inexperience flung in her face.

'Thirty-three. That's not so old. Whereas you're . . .?'

'Twenty-four.'

The back of his hand trailed along her jaw line. 'What's wrong with those fellows down in Arizona that they've let a woman like you get away?'

'Bringing up the kids and all, I haven't had much time for socialising and dating,' she explained carefully, not wanting to sound as if she was whining about what fate had dealt her, but at the same time not wanting him to think that her lack of experience was due to men finding her unattractive.

'Life had been pretty tough for you, hasn't it?'

Maggie brushed aside his pity. 'Others have it worse. Besides, the hard times are mostly behind us. Bayard has a good job and Julie will be off to college next autumn.' She changed the subject. 'You never did tell me why you woke me up.'

'I was a little side-tracked.' He grinned at the blush that reddened her cheekbones. 'Listen.'

'I don't hear anything.'

'Exactly.'

Maggie bounced off the bed and ran to the enormous window in the living-room. Spread before her eyes was a winter wonderland, every inch of the landscape carpeted in glistening white. Across the valley rose majestic mountains, their peaks dyed peach by the same setting sun that painted the icy blue sky with streaks of pink and fuchsia. Her breath caught in her throat. 'It's absolutely beautiful.' Outside the window was an enormous deck drifted with snow. Footsteps led across the deck to a small wooden platform. Even as Maggie spotted it, a small grey squirrel scampered down a pine tree, dislodging powdery clumps of snow, and made his way across a railing to the platform. There was food on the platform and the tiny animal stuffed several handfuls into his mouth before a large grey bird scared him away when it landed with a loud squawk. 'Bully,' she said softly, not wanting to startle the bird. 'Scaring away a baby squirrel.'

'That wasn't a baby, it was a chickaree, the smallest tree squirrel we have in these parts,' Nick said in her ear. 'He'll be back. They all know where the hand-outs come from. Can you hear that stuttering sound?' At her nod, he said, 'That's him swearing at the camp-robber.'

'Camp-robber?'

'The grey jay. He's so bold that he'll come right down to your campsite and steal food off the table. Look how fat he is. Air under his feathers act like insulation to keep him warm. One of the best parts of owning this cabin is watching the wildlife. The couple who watch the cabin for me keep the feeders supplied when I'm not around.' He pointed to a small masked bird with a rosy chest hanging upside-down on a mesh bag pecking at the contents. 'There's one of my favourite visitors.'

'He's darling. A chickadee?'

Nick shook his head. 'A red-breasted nuthatch. Though I've no doubt some chickadees will be along soon.'

'What's that he's eating?'

'Beef suet.'

'Ugh. Not my idea of a gourmet meal. Look! Another one.'

Nick grinned. 'Now that is a chickadee.' He walked over to the bookcase, returning with a small book. 'Here's a book on birds. Why don't you see who you can identify while I scare us up some dinner.'

'Something better than suet, I hope.' Maggie

wrinkled her nose expressively.

While Nick banged around dishes and pans and created delicious smells that eddied in from the kitchen, Maggie kept up a running commentary on the visitors to the feeder. Archie stood beside her at the window, his nose quivering with interest. As the sun sank further down below the horizon those visiting the deck became fewer and fewer until only a couple of grey juncoes remained, digging in the snow for the seed that had spilled to the floor of the deck. Maggie closed the bird-book with a regretful sigh. 'Well, I guess that's that.'

'For now, anyway,' Nick agreed. 'The night visitors will come later. The deer-mice and sometimes a pack-rat.'

'No wonder you bought this place,' Maggie said, sighing with pleasure. 'It's as if you're cut off from the rest of the world in your own private oasis. No blare of rock music, no yelling kids, no roar of traffic, no ringing phones. Just peace and quiet. My idea of heaven.'

'No television.'

'I rest my case. Peace and quiet. If you knew how Bayard and Julie fight over what programme they're going to watch. You asked what I'd do with more money. Buy a second television,' she said with heartfelt conviction.

Nick laughed. 'It's not so quiet in the summer. The road is open then, with lots of tourists heading over Independence Pass to Aspen.' He slanted a teasing look in her direction. 'Luckily most of them don't drop in for a visit.'

'Unfair. I've already admitted that I acted stupidly and I've apologised profusely for disturbing you and thanked you repeatedly for coming to my rescue.

What more do you want?' Spotting the wicked gleam in his eyes, she hastily changed the subject. 'I wonder what Bayard and his friends have been doing. Do you think that they had the same snowstorm?'

'It's hard to tell. Sometimes the mountains act as a barrier, keeping a storm on one side or the other. I wish that the storm hadn't knocked out the phone lines, so that you could let him know you're OK.' He set plates on the table.

'He won't have given me a thought,' Maggie said. 'Besides . . .' her voice trailed off.

'Besides?' Nick prompted.

'I'm not sure that Bayard would understand what I'm doing all alone in a cabin with a strange man,' she said carefully.

Nick tightened his lips momentarily before asking, 'Would you have preferred that I left you to freeze to death?'

'No, of course not, it's just that . . .'

'You're embarrassed,' he guessed, his back to her as he stirred the contents of a pan on the stove.

'Naturally I'm embarrassed that I acted impulsively and then stupidly. Who wouldn't be? But that's not what you mean, is it? You're referring to undressing me and holding me against your nude body. I guess, in a way, I am embarrassed by that, but rather a little embarrassment than freezing to death. It's just that, well, Bayard and Julie might not see it that way. Death before dishonour and all that,' she added lightly.

'I don't recall dishonouring you,' he said coldly, turning to impale her with an icy glare.

'You didn't,' she said quickly. 'I'm not explaining myself very well. I'm their older sister, and Julie and Bayard, well, they have expectations about how I should act.'

His face softened. 'Like when I was in high school and my mother wore a sexy dress to a party. I was appalled.'

She nodded, grateful for his understanding. 'I guess you could say I've been their surrogate mother.'

'Then they certainly wouldn't approve of my kissing you,' he teased, turning back to his cooking-chores.

'Or my kissing you back.' Maggie hesitated. 'I'm glad they won't know, because their disapproval would somehow spoil the memory of our kisses.' She faced his broad back defiantly. 'I enjoyed having you kiss me. I suppose that a woman shouldn't admit that to a strange man, but in a crazy kind of way, I feel it's rather silly to play games and be less than honest when I know that you know the location of every freckle on my body. Besides, once I leave here, we'll never see each other again. So, if you want to laugh at me for admitting that I liked kissing you, go ahead, but the comment stands.'

Nick froze at the stove before saying quietly, 'I wouldn't think of laughing at you; I'm honoured by your trusting me with the truth.' Handing Maggie a steaming bowl, he added gravely, 'I enjoyed kissing you, too.' It wasn't until all the food was on the table that he added, 'Actually, I probably know about a few freckles that you aren't aware of. I can't imagine how you could possibly see the one . . .'

'Never mind,' Maggie hastily interrupted him, warned by the glint in his eyes in what direction his remark was headed. 'Now that the snow has stopped, will you help me find my car and spring me loose from the drifts?'

'There's no hurry. You're not going anywhere until the snowplough clears the road up to the barricades. In the morning will be early enough to look for your car.'

Maggie looked at him in dismay. 'In the morning? What about tonight? If you think that just because I said I liked to kiss you, that's an open invitation to share your bed.' She blinked at the vulgar word he bit out.

'We have been penned in here together for almost twenty-four hours with you entirely at my mercy, and I haven't raped you yet. What makes you think that just because the sun goes down I'm going to start?'

Maggie ventured an apologetic smile. 'I guess librarians have vivid imaginations because we read so much.'

'If that's an apology, I accept it. And furthermore, I'll even volunteer to be the one who sleeps on the couch tonight.'

The dinner that Nick had magically conjured up from canned goods and a small freezer might not have been gourmet but it tasted delicious to Maggie. After they had shared the clean-up chores, and given Archie the choice of titbits they had saved for him, they sat in front of a roaring fire and played cards. Nick was well educated and knowledgeable on a wide variety of subjects and Maggie was pleased to discover that they had read many of the same authors. Not that they always agreed on their criticisms. In fact, their opinions differed on a variety of subjects, but their arguments were amiable, Nick willing to listen to Maggie's ideas. He spoke of some of the wildlife visitors that he had had at the cabin and asked Maggie more about her family. She was able to laugh at some of the tales that hadn't seemed so amusing at the time.

'You've carried an amazing load,' Nick observed.

Maggie brushed away his remark. 'It sounds trite, but one does what one has to do. Anyway, now that the kids are pretty well grown up, I'm going to have so much free time I won't know what to do with myself.'

'You could get married.'

'Pooh. And exchange one prison for another? No way. I'm looking forward to glorious freedom, long soaks in bubble bath and travel, lots of travel. Who knows? I might even find the time to make my fortune.'

'You could marry for it. Isn't that the time-honoured method?'

'Easily said. But I don't exactly run in moneyed circles.'

'Rich men read, too, you know.'

'I can hardly ask to see their bank cards as well as their library cards, can I? Besides,' she shrugged, 'everyone knows rich men marry rich women, or at least beautiful women. You know the type of woman I mean. Coal-black hair or platinum blondes, Madonna faces, perfect shoulders, and especially swan-like necks.' She thrust her head into the air. 'See. Hardly swan-like. And don't forget the red hair.'

'I'm not likely to. But I fail to see the importance of the swan-like neck,' he said in amusement.

'To show off the diamonds, of course. Six-inch dog-collars of diamonds around their necks and yards of the stuff hanging from their ears.'

'It sounds rather gaudy to me. Is that what you'd like? Yards of diamonds?'

'Don't be silly,' she said disdainfully. 'I'm a

red-head. I dream of being showered with emeralds. To match my eyes.'

'Your eyes are more turquoise than green.'

'What a spoilsport you are. If I can pretend I'm rich, I can pretend I have green eyes, can't I? It's *my* fantasy.'

'If you're pretending, why not be a blonde, since you seem to think blonde is so beautiful?'

'Like Julie, you mean. She has the loveliest ash-blonde hair, like my mother.'

Just then Archie whined to go out and Nick stood up to answer the dog's summons. 'Your sister is blonde?' he asked in surprise. 'For some reason, I was picturing Little Orphan Annie.'

Maggie yawned. 'There is no one who looks less like an orphaned moppet than Julie, believe me. She truly intends to marry rich, and she probably will.'

'I take it she had the requisite swan-like neck,' Nick said drily, letting Archie back inside and towelling him dry.

Maggie nodded, standing up. 'Can I help you make up the sofa?'

For an answer, Nick tossed her sheets from a closet, and the sofa was quickly opened up and made into a bed. Disappearing into the bedroom Nick came out carrying a bundle of clothes. 'Do you want the pyjamas or the nightshirt?'

'Which ever you don't want.'

He handed her the nightshirt. 'Sleep well.'

If only she could. She shouldn't have taken a nap this afternoon. Then she would be tired instead of lying in bed wide awake and aware of every sound Nick made as he moved around the living-room. She could hear him talking softly to Archie and then the creak of springs as he settled down on the sofa.

Maggie stared at the light seeping around the edges of the partially closed door. The sofa wasn't visible from her vantage point, and she wondered what he was doing when the lights didn't go off. Reading maybe. Nick's books were well thumbed. She should tell him that dog-earing the corners was bad for books. She should go to sleep is what she should do.

Turning on her side, Maggie plumped up her pillow, but sleep continued to be elusive. Her thoughts kept returning to the taste of Nick's mouth, the warmth of his skin, the feel of his hand covering her breast. A hundred new sensations she had experienced today. At first they had been pleasant, but pleasant had quickly turned into something she couldn't define. It wasn't that she hadn't enjoyed Nick's kisses, because she had. The problem was, those kisses only made her hungry for more.

Restlessly, Maggie tossed and turned. If only she weren't Maggie Russell, practical, sensible, cautious, never one to rush headlong into folly. Why couldn't she be the type who gambled on life? She thought of the girls who had come to her in the library for advice. That had been a laugh. What did she know of human sexuality? They had wanted personal guidance. She had sent them to the book stacks.

In the next room was a man who she felt sure could teach her all she had ever wanted to know about sex. What would it be like to have Nick make love to her? To have his body bare against hers again, only this time, not merely to warm her up but to set her aflame? And he could do it. Some womanly instinct deep within her told her that Nick had the power to raise her to undreamed-of heights of pleasure. What if she never encountered such a man again? Never experienced the total fulfilment of being a woman? Would she be sorry when she was sixty-two and had never known the exquisite pleasures of making love to a man like Nick? Did she want to spend the rest of her life asking, 'Why didn't I?'

'Maggie, are you asleep?' Nick stood in the bedroom doorway, a large shadowy figure.

Maggie clutched the blankets up under her chin. 'No.'

'I think we have some nocturnal visitors. Come out here if you're interested.'

Tucking a blanket around her to ward off the night chill, Maggie padded out to the living-room. She stopped short on the threshold. Nick was wearing only the pyjama bottoms, his upper torso disturbingly bare. He gestured impatiently at her, and she moved on into the room as he turned off the overhead lights and guided her to the window. Quietly he pulled aside the curtains.

Outside a full moon bathed the snow-covered landscape with soft light, while a gentle breeze flirted with the pine trees, creating dancing shadows on the white ground. 'I don't see anything.'

'Just wait,' Nick said softly. 'They were here a minute ago. I heard them. They'll be back.'

So close to the window, Maggie could feel the insidious cold creeping through the large expanse of glass, and she thought of Nick's bare skin. She gulped. 'Would you like to share my blanket?'

'I thought you'd never ask,' Nick teased as he took the end she held out and wrapped it around himself, snuggling her close in front of him in the process.

The heat from his body seared her skin through the flannel nightshirt, and she could feel his heart pulsing against her back. He rested his chin on her head and his breath stirred her hair. Tightly encased in his embrace, she allowed herself to pretend that they were other than two ships passing in the night. In a perfect world, she would not have to drive off in the morning never to see him again.

Never in her wildest imagination could she have conjured up a man like him. Quick-thinking and capable, he had saved her life. But more than his rescue drew her to him. She felt him to be a kindred spirit in the way that he had shouldered the responsibilities of his family's business. He was a man that a woman could depend on, could lean upon when her own burdens grew too heavy. Not to mention his dark good looks, the fact that he was a creditable cook, had a nice sense of humour, was an interesting and charming companion, and his body put out heat like a raging furnace. She felt warm and glowing, as if her bones were going to melt. One of Nick's hands was pressed against her stomach and now a thumb began inscribing slow, sensuous circles on top of the flannel. Maggie's breathing quickened while an unfamiliar tension began building inside her beneath the warmth of his hand.

Nick stiffened; his hand tensed against her body. 'There.' One minute the feeder on the deck was empty, the next minute four pairs of large eyes seemed to be staring at her. 'Deer-mice,' Nick breathed behind her.

Maggie watched in fascination as the small creatures greedily gobbled up seed, their large ears twitching. 'They are darling,' she whispered.

'I knew you'd enjoy seeing them,' he said in satisfaction, his lips close to her ear. 'I . . .' Suddenly a loud sneeze shattered the peaceful scene. In a blink of an eye the deck was empty. 'Sorry,' Nick apologised.

'Your hair was tickling my nose.'

She giggled. 'I hope those poor little guys don't die of fright.'

Nick let the curtains drop back in place in front of the window. 'So much for tonight's show, Ladies and Gentlemen.'

'Won't they be back?' Maggie asked in disappointment, reluctant to leave Nick's arms.

'I'm sure they will. All that free food is too good to pass up.' He made no move to unwrap the blanket that harnessed them together. 'Maggie.' His voice changed; there was a low, teasing, seductive quality to it.

'What?' She could scarcely breathe.

'I have this awful urge to make a terrible joke about librarians getting between the covers.'

'Restrain yourself.'

'You don't know how hard that is with you nestled in my arms.'

'Yes, I do,' she said breathlessly. She had known from the minute she had offered to share her blanket with him. The entire time they had been standing in front of the window, his hands, his arms, his entire body had been informing her of his wants and needs. Wants and needs shared by her.

Hands on her shoulders, Nick slowly turned her to face him. He swept a straying tendril from her cheek, his hand brushing warmly against her skin. 'It was difficult enough to fall asleep last night; tonight it's proving impossible.'

She barely grasped the meaning of his muted words as his breath kissed her lips an infinitesimal moment before his mouth covered hers. If his body had been warm against her back, it was searing against her front. As Nick deepened the kiss, Maggie swayed weakly within his embrace, her boneless body of little support. The skin of his upper body was molten silk beneath her hands and she was unable to curb the impulse that sent fingers exploring, twining their way through a heavy mat of chest hair, homing in on small nipples that hardened at her touch.

The heat in the cabin was scorching and the hot, clinging blanket was suffocating her. With an impatient twitch of her body, she sent it falling to the floor. As a bid to cool off, it proved futile as Nick loosened the front of her nightshirt and slipped it off one shoulder, exposing a wide expanse of throbbing skin to his heated lips. A cauldron of scalding emotions flamed through her body. The nightshirt slid lower. Taking a strand of her hair, Nick brushed it slowly across a bare breast before curling it around the swollen nipple.

Piercingly sweet torment. Her breath came in gasps and her heart was pounding. She could barely think, overcome by the strange and potent yearnings that Nick aroused in her. She longed for fulfilment. Would one night of love be so wrong? Who would ever know? They would never see each other again. Ahead of her was a fork in the road. One trail was safe, familiar. The other led to uncharted regions. Maggie had always chosen the safe, the known.

'You aren't real,' Nick said in a thickened voice. 'You're a red-haired witch who's cast her spell over me. But the joke is on you, because I have no intention of letting you escape me. Ever.' Pressing his lips fiercely against hers, he grasped the thin nightshirt with his hands and yanked it the length of her body. 'You said that your sister and brother don't need you any more. I do.'

The cold block of ice that immediately formed in

the pit of Maggie's stomach had nothing to do with her lack of clothing. Nick's stripping the clothing from her body had also stripped the shutters from her mind. What was she doing? Surrendering her self-respect for a night of pleasure? Tearing her lips from his, she pushed frantically on his bare chest. 'I can't,' she choked. 'This is a terrible mistake. I . . . I don't want to . . . to make . . . to do this,' she stammered. 'I'm sorry . . .' The words caught in her throat as she felt the angry stiffening of his body, his hands tightening on her bare hips. Heaven help her, his hands felt so right there. She was afraid to look at him, afraid to move for fear of driving him into actions they would both regret.

'I called you a tantalising witch, but I was wrong, wasn't I? You're not a witch at all. Although there is a name for a woman like you. A name that sounds remarkably like witch,' he sneered. Stooping with abrupt, angry movements, he grabbed the blanket from the floor and threw it at her. 'Cover yourself up,' he ordered, his voice raw with emotion.

Silently Maggie obeyed, her shaking limbs chilled by the loss of his body heat. She could hardly blame him for being angry. Her body begged her to forget her inhibitions, to ignore the moral code which denied her fulfilment. 'I'm . . . I'm sorry,' she stammered again, knowing that her apology was meaningless in the face of her outrageous behaviour.

'Go to bed.'

'I didn't mean to . . .'

'Bed!' he roared, 'Unless . . .' He captured her arm, his grip painfully tight as he hauled her face close to his. 'Maybe you want to be persuaded. Such enthusiasm as you exhibited can hardly be turned off like a tap.'

A sick dread crawled along her backbone as she numbly shook her head. 'I . . . I'm sorry,' she repeated helplessly.

He tossed her arm away from him as if he couldn't bear the touch of her skin. 'Go to bed,' he forced out between clenched teeth, 'or I won't be responsible for my actions.'

Maggie went, his threat that they would talk in the morning ringing in her ears.

Long after Nick's soft snores filled the living-room, Maggie lay stiff and unmoving in his bedroom. She couldn't blame Nick for hating her for what she had done. She had gone willingly into his arms; he hadn't forced her. He had every reason to believe that she intended to tumble into bed with him. The truth was, she had considered it, even wanted it. Nick's reference to her brother and a sister had jolted her back to reality. How many times had she cautioned Julie against allowing her emotions to override her common sense? A woman didn't fall into bed with a man, any man, even one as attractive as Nick, merely to satisfy a sexual itch.

The pillow was stone beneath her head. How could she face Nick in the morning? Suppose he decided to take up where they had left off? She had come to her senses in time tonight, but would she be so sensible in the morning? If he decided that she was simply playing hard to get, would she be able to resist his sensual persuasion? Honesty forced her to face the fact that her resistance to Nick was practically nil. He wasn't the type of man to force her, but he wouldn't have to. Her body still trembled with longing.

She shuddered. Morning would bring the promised—no, the threatened—discussion. Practical, sensible Maggie Russell suddenly found

herself in waters far out of her depth. Nothing in her
life had prepared her for a man like Nick. If she had
been the sensible woman that everyone believed her
to be, she would run from him as far and as fast as
she could. At first light Maggie was up and on her
way, leaving Nick sound asleep on the sofa.

CHAPTER FOUR

MAGGIE'S driveway was a welcoming sight after the sweltering drive home through dense traffic. The late May wind blowing off the desert had offered little relief. Spring fever was running rampant among the children in the school library and today had been a particularly challenging one. It seemed as if overnight the children that she had always enjoyed had become impossible changelings. She turned off the ignition and sat wearily behind the wheel. The children hadn't changed. She had. Their spring fever wasn't a patch on the uncontrolled yearnings that stirred within her breast. Restless, discontented. Ever since Christmas vacation she had been unable to settle to anything, and it didn't take a genius to know why. Nick had introduced her to a whole new world of fascinating sensations. In the hopes of curbing some of her restlessness, she had accepted a few dates from some of the male faculty. Rejecting their advances had been all too easy. If wasn't what Nick had taught her that she missed. It was Nick.

Her last sight of him was seared into her memory. The urge to pull the blankets up over his shoulders, kissing warm, bare skin in the process had been overwhelming, but then he had muttered something and she had quickly said she was letting Archie out. He had told her to hurry. She had hurried all right. Away from him. Away from the spell that he had cast over her. She wasn't the witch. If she stayed it would have been contemptibly easy for Nick to

73

persuade her into his bed. It certainly hadn't required much effort on his part to persuade her into his arms. She cringed inwardly as she thought of her shameless behaviour.

Leaving Nick's cabin, Maggie had driven straight back to Tucson. When Julie and Bayard had returned from their respective holidays, the kitchen was painted, the dining-room walls were papered. Not one word had Maggie ever uttered about her rash, impulsive decision to drive to Aspen. How could she have been so irresponsible? The whole episode was one she wanted to blot from her memory. Unfortunately a dark head of hair in the distance, the sound of the wind, even a man's laugh from across a room sent her thoughts zooming directly to Nick.

She wondered what he had thought when he had finally awoken and found her gone. Guilt over taking the money flooded her. She had been in a panic when she discovered her wallet was missing from her jacket. She must have lost it floundering about in the snow. There had been no time to look for it. Quickly subtracting some notes from Nick's wallet, she had left him a hasty note of explanation. She hoped he had understood. Returning the money to him had turned out to be impossible.

Maggie brushed a hand across her sweaty forehead. It would be nice if her car had an air-conditioner on such a warm day. Another luxury that she couldn't afford. Her dress was sticking to her back and the hair that had escaped from its rigid bun was frizzed around her face. She was glad that Bayard had kitchen duty tonight, even if that did mean hamburgers cooked outside on the grill. It was too hot to turn on the stove anyway.

The minute Maggie stepped into the living-room she knew that something was terribly wrong. Bayard and Julie sat side by side on the sofa, twin monuments to pain and despair. Both looked up at her entrance, hope momentarily overriding their distress. Julie's aqua eyes were rimmed in red, her lashes drenched with tears.

Maggie dropped her briefcase on a nearby chair. 'What is it?' she asked sharply. 'What's the matter?'

'He couldn't help himself, Maggie,' Julie cried. 'He'll pay it all back.'

Maggie turned to her brother in confusion. The half-pleading, half-defiant look on his face sent a chill of premonition down her spine. 'Bayard?'

'I'm sorry, Maggie. It was so easy . . . I just didn't think.'

'What was easy?' Maggie probed, completely bewildered.

'I stole some money from the shop,' he admitted in a low voice.

Maggie fell into the nearest chair, refusing to believe what he had said. 'That's impossible. You couldn't have.'

Bayard looked at her with misery-filled eyes. 'I saw this loophole in the accounting system, and at first it was just an experiment, but it was so easy . . . so I did it again. I don't know what came over me. It was like a game. I didn't even think about the consequences.'

Maggie shook her head numbly. This had to be a nightmare. 'Stealing . . .' When Bayard had landed the job in the business office at Ryan's, the three of them had been thrilled. Ryan's in Tucson was only one of a large chain of up-market department stores located all over the West. With Bayard's brains, Maggie had felt sure that he would go far, but now

. . . stealing. Maggie pushed aside her anger. That would have to wait until later. Now it was important to get to the bottom of what had happened. 'I take it you got caught.'

Bayard nodded. 'I intended to pay it back, but first, I thought, a new car. With a rise in a couple of weeks . . .' his voice trailed off before Maggie's look of horror. Clearing his throat, he switched from self-justification to what had taken place at work that day. When the theft was discovered, the big boss, Mr Ryan himself, had been in town, and he had come to Bayard's office with Bayard's supervisor. At first Mr Ryan had been content to let the local man do the questioning, but then he had seen Julie's picture on Bayard's desk. From that moment on, the tone of the investigation had changed. The local store manager had been dismissed, and Mr Ryan had given Bayard a fantastic ultimatum. He might forget the whole matter if Bayard sent his sister in.

'I told Bayard I'd go,' Julie said stoutly, her pale face disclosing what those words had cost her. 'Maybe I can persuade him to let Bayard pay back the money and forget the whole thing.'

'No,' Maggie said immediately. Just thinking about it sent a sickening shudder throughout Maggie's body. Mr Ryan might have wrapped the offer up in fancy words, but the blunt truth was, Bayard's sister in exchange for clemency.

Bayard echoed her response. 'I told Mr Ryan 'no deal' this afternoon, but he said I had to come home and discuss it with my sister. I shouldn't even have told her, but when I came in this afternoon, she knew something was wrong, and well, you know how she is. She had the truth from me before I could think,' he said apologetically to Maggie.

Maggie knew how it was. Julie had always been the stronger of the two. 'It's out of the question,' she said abstractedly, her mind blindly groping for the solution to this horror that Bayard had plunged them into.

Julie was not easily persuaded. All evening a long battle had raged between her and Bayard, Julie adamant to play Joan of Arc and save Bayard while Bayard was just as determined to keep his sister out of it, saying he wouldn't have her humiliated because of his actions. Maggie hadn't been able to refrain from pointing out that if Bayard really cared about humiliating his sister, he wouldn't have committed a crime that could land him in prison, thereby disgracing his entire family.

By the time Maggie fell into bed that night she knew what she had to do. Go see this Mr Ryan herself. The more Maggie considered the matter, the less she believed that an important man like Mr Ryan would make such a proposition. Terrified at being caught, Bayard must have misunderstood something that his boss had said. He was still scared and persuading him to let Maggie go in to see his boss had not been difficult.

Lying in bed, Maggie plotted what she would say the next morning. She must persuade the store that restitution of the missing funds better suited their purpose than prosecuting Bayard. Once they understood that Bayard knew he had been wrong and had been so severely frightened by the enormity of his offence, surely they would go easy on him. If she had to, she would play on every sympathetic feeling Mr Ryan had ever had by bringing up Bayard's tragic past. On the other hand, if Mr Ryan was the lascivious old man conjured up by the idea of his offer, Maggie intended to inform him in no uncertain terms what he could do with his offer. Not that she excused what Bayard had done, but no matter how angry she was with him, no matter how wrong he was, he was still her brother and she would fight for him. The day her grandmother had learned that her illness was terminal she had called Maggie into her bedroom and told her that now Maggie was responsible for Bayard and Julie. She wouldn't let her grandmother down.

Maggie felt as if her stomach were tied in one tremendous knot the next morning as she sat in a modern office waiting to be shown into Mr Ryan's presence. Useless to continue asking herself why Bayard had done it. If only she had seen how important money and the things it could buy were to him. Perhaps if she had been more understanding, less judgemental about how he spent his pay, he might have come to her and they could have worked out something to buy him a new car. Would this Mr Ryan remember how it was to be twenty-three and desperately wanting to impress the girls? Bayard hadn't given her many clues as to what type of man he was. Middle-aged, cold, stern, unforgiving was how Bayard had described him. Well, what did he expect from a man he had cheated?

'Mr Ryan will see you now.' The secretary held open a door.

Maggie closed her eyes and took a deep breath. There was no putting if off. She walked through the doorway into the lion's den.

The man leaning forward on the enormous desk stared coldly at her. 'Who the hell are you supposed to be?'

'You! What are you doing here? I expected to see Mr Ryan.' He looked so good to her that she had an insane desire to run and fling her arms around him.

Nick inclined his head one-eighth of an inch. 'I'm Ryan.'

'It's me. Maggie,' she said weakly. He didn't even remember her. 'Don't you recognise me?'

'I should, shouldn't I, Red? The resemblance to your brother is striking. Not to mention the same thieving habits.'

'Didn't you find my note?' Maggie cried. 'I tried to return the money. I called Information in Denver to get your phone number but Nick Peters wasn't listed. Now I see why,' she added bitterly, fumbling in her bag. 'As soon as I got home I put the money here in case I ever figured out how to get it to you.' Her hand shaking, she thrust the folded notes at him. 'Here.'

He eyed the money with contempt, refusing to touch it. She dropped it to the floor. 'Did you ever consider waiting until I got up before you left? Why didn't you wake me and ask for the money?'

'I . . . I had my reasons,' she mumbled.

'Take off those damn glasses.'

She stared at him in surprise before complying. She had forgotten how she was dressed. When she had started at the high school library her youth and inexperience had made her a natural target for the teasing of the older boys and she had taken to wearing clear-glass lenses with horn-rims and skimming her hair back into a bun in an effort to look older. Gradually the boys had forgotten what was hidden behind the disguise and saw her only as a librarian. This morning she had donned her severest suit in an effort to impress Mr Ryan with her maturity and to convince him that Bayard came from a responsible, law-abiding family.

'Now the hair.' His voice was coldly implacable.

Her hands were shaking so badly that she could barely find the hairpins. With a muttered oath he strode across the room and ripped the pins from her hair. Tears sprang to her eyes at his rough treatment but she didn't dare object, for fear he would rip her hair out. She could feel the anger burning within him. If he had ever shown her this aspect of his personality while she had been at the cabin he would have terrified her. He terrified her now.

'I told Don, your brother's boss, that I have a personal interest in this matter with your brother. He'll be discreet. It hasn't left this office. Whether it does is up to you.' He was back seated behind the desk, leaving her standing awkwardly in front of it.

She felt like a miscreant child in the principal's office, and she was aware that he wanted her to feel at a disadvantage. Her chin lifted a notch in defiance. 'We plan to repay the . . . the debt.'

'You bet you will,' he growled softly, the menace thick in his voice.

She dug in her purse again. 'We . . . we worked out a repayment plan. If this is satisfactory to you.' She held the papers out to him.

He ignored them, tapping a pencil against his teeth, taking his time to answer, allowing the suspense to build within her. His gaze insolently travelled the length of her body. 'You looked a damn sight better in my nightshirt than you do in that rag.' Not allowing her to comment on his unexpected remark, he rolled the heavy office chair up to the desk and placed his hands flat on the wooden surface. 'Here's the deal. You for your brother. Straight across.'

Maggie gasped. Bayard hadn't misunderstood.

This was insane. Not Nick. She stared at him in dismay. 'What do you mean?' The words were barely audible.

'I get you. He goes free.'

'You can't be serious.'

He shrugged. 'Think about the alternatives. A pretty guy like him in prison. He'll be a hit with the lifers.'

Cold horror held her in its grip and she sank into the nearest chair. 'Why . . . are . . . are you doing . . . why?' she asked in a trembling voice.

'Why?' He slammed his fist down on the desk. 'You have the nerve to ask me why? Your damned brother stole money from me. That's not exactly legal, Red. Of course, since you're a thief, too, maybe you don't see the immorality of it.'

'I admit that what he did was wrong, but . . .'

'You think that he should get off scot-free?' he demanded.

'No, but . . .'

'No buts. You or him. Which is it?'

'What do you want from me?' she whispered.

He grinned malevolently at her. 'I've been thinking that over ever since you walked into this office. What would you hate the most? I think I've come up with the perfect answer.'

Maggie's stomach heaved as she looked at the mask of devilish mockery on his face. Palpable waves of anger reached across the desk and battered her already lacerated emotions. 'Wh . . . what?'

His eyes narrowed. 'I dreamt about the day that I'd have you in my power. You won't find me so easy to shove from your arms this time.' The glint in his eye acknowledged her involuntary start at his words. 'A red-haired witch who pretended that she was going to share her magic until she disappeared into a puff of smoke.' He studied her in silence a few moments before continuing, 'You won't disappear this time, Red. This time I've caught you and I have no intention of letting you escape.'

She waited uneasily as he coldly appraised her, the swift-beating pulse in her throat threatening to choke her.

Leaning back in the heavy leather chair, he twirled a pencil in his hand, never taking his eyes from her. 'We're getting married.'

'Married! But marriage is for ever.'

'Exactly.'

'No. I can't. I won't!'

The pencil continued to twirl. 'Maybe you'd like to discuss it with your brother before you decide,' he suggested, the implication clear in his cool words.

Maggie closed her eyes, waves of despair washing over her. His threats to Bayard left her with no choice. There was no question of her brother's guilt, and even though it was Bayard's first offence, Nick was powerful, and fighting him would be futile. She couldn't risk Bayard being sent to prison. She opened her eyes. Nick had moved around the desk and was standing in front of her. 'All right.' She cleared her throat. 'I'll marry you.'

Iron clamps on her shoulders forced her to stand. 'Let me be the first to kiss the blushing bride,' Nick said sarcastically.

Maggie stood stoically, accepting that from now on it was he who controlled her life. His kiss was hard and fierce, pressing against her lips with such force that she could feel her teeth cutting into her tender gums. If he hoped that she would fight him or beg for mercy, he was wrong. She wouldn't give him the satisfaction. Passively she opened her mouth to his demands. Then an odd thing happened. Her body began to remember the passion they had shared, and she melted into his arms, her lips returning his kisses with a fervour that spoke of the lonely, endless nights when she had longed for him to take her in his arms and ease the ache of desire to which he had introduced her. The tantalising scent of his skin and the familiar taste of his mouth were aphrodisiacs that exploded the control she had placed on her emotions, and she pressed frantically against his body, her frenzied hands running wildly through his silky black hair. An angry buzzing sound in her ear.

Nick thrust her away, dragging his lips from hers. 'The phone,' he said hoarsely.

Embarrassed and shaken by her response to his kiss, Maggie turned blindly away. Behind her Nick muttered a few words into the phone and then slammed it down. She faced him at the sound of her name. He was behind the desk, the expression on his face unreadable, as he leaned forward, balancing his weight on two balled fists resting on the desk. 'Leave your phone number and address with the secretary. I'll be by tonight to make plans.'

She nodded, dry-eyed. The pain was too intense for tears. 'What shall I tell the kids?'

'Your brother's not a kid. He's a grown man. Tell him the truth.'

'No. I don't want him to know. He . . . he wouldn't let me sacrifice myself for him.'

Nick dropped into the chair and swept up a pile of papers. 'Tell him whatever you want,' he said dismissively as he began thumbing through the pile.

Maggie wheeled about and groped for the door handle.

His cold voice stopped her. 'Just out of curiosity, Red, how did you get your car out?'

She refused to face him. 'The snowplough. The man clearing the road had just reached the barrier when I got there. He had chains and pulled me out.' She waited a second, but when there was no response, she left, closing the door carefully behind her. At least he hadn't asked about Julie.

Driving home after her meeting with Nick, Maggie tried to concentrate on what she was going to say to Bayard and Julie but Nick filled her thoughts. He had called her a thief and his bargain to spare Bayard was undeniably brutal, but all she could think about was how good it felt to be in his arms. Which was as crazy as this proposed marriage, especially as it was obvious that he retained no fond memories of her. A quiver of fear raced up her spine. The cold, angry Nick Ryan whom she had just left was a world removed from the teasing, laughing Nick Peters she had known in Colorado. Why was Nick Ryan insisting that she marry him?

Whatever his reasons, at least in his anger and the shock of seeing Maggie, he had completely forgotten his initial demand to meet Julie. What would he say when he came to the house tonight and saw her? Lovely Julie. Maggie's heart jolted to a stop. What if Nick demanded her instead of Maggie? Julie mustn't be sacrificed to pay for Bayard's crime.

She pounded the steering-wheel with her clenched fist. Bayard! How could he have been so criminally stupid? He could have ruined his whole life with just a few punches of a button. And for a stupid car. He was her brother and she would protect him, but that didn't erase the fact that she was furious with him. Other young men had lost their parents, had been brought up in homes where money was scarce and they had turned out just fine. Maybe Bayard was weak because he had been brought up in a family of women. Being the only boy, he had been indulged by both her and Nana.

Now Maggie had to make sure that Bayard understood that she would never again save him from the consequences of his own behaviour. Nor would Julie. It was one thing to save Bayard herself; she would not allow Julie to be sacrificed. Maggie thrust her fingers through her loosened hair, hoping to erase the pain in her throbbing head. The store's cleaning service would wonder about the hairpins all over the carpet if Nick didn't pick them up. Her thoughts tumbled over each other like panicked squirrels in a cage. She was only twenty-four years old. Too young to have the responsibility of a grown family in her hands. Damn Bayard. How could he have done this to them?

By the time the doorbell rang that evening the pain in Maggie's head had mushroomed to such a degree that she scarcely knew what she was doing. Even worse, she hadn't said a word to Bayard and Julie about marrying Nick. All she had told Bayard was that she had persuaded the store not to press charges if he agreed to restitution. When he had wanted to know every little detail as well as offer further excuses for his behaviour her nerves had exploded in a display of temper that quickly had him retreating from the dinner-table. His withdrawal was quickly followed by Julie's storming dramatically from the dining-room after she had made the mistake of accusing Maggie of selfishly usurping Julie's role as Bayard's saviour.

If her head hadn't ached so fiercely, Maggie might

have appreciated the humour in the pathetic scene
that greeted Nick when she showed him into the
living-room. Only Archie was happy to see Nick,
erupting into an explosive welcome as soon as he
recognised him. Julie, in the role of a long-suffering,
much-maligned sister, barely looked up, while
Bayard was visibly disturbed by Nick's unexpected
appearance. Maggie knew she looked terrible, still
wearing the unattractive suit, her hair back in its
accustomed bun, her face pale without make-up.

A faint twitch at the corner of Nick's mouth
betrayed his amusement. Looking briefly at her in
the room's harsh light, he said, for her ears alone, as
he bent over Archie, calming the dog down, 'You
look like hell,'

So much for the amenities. 'Thank you,' Maggie
said sweetly. 'It's in your honour, of course.'

He uttered a sharp laugh. 'You forgot to kiss me
hello, Red.' Straightening up, he pulled her into his
arms, kissing her with a thoroughness that left her
trembling. The triumphant gleam in his eyes as he
released her was all the proof that she needed that the
kiss was in retaliation for her insult. Before she could
protest, he crossed the room to Julie. 'I see that Red
didn't lie when she told me how beautiful her little
sister was.' He gathered up Julie's small hand in his
enormous ones. 'I'm Nick Ryan. You new brother-
in-law to be.'

If eyes could pop out, then Julie's and Bayard's
were in danger of doing so. Maggie felt like throwing
herself down on the floor and indulging in a fit of
hysterics. Nick's eyes knifed across the room at her
before he turned back to Julie. 'I guess Red hasn't
got around to making the big announcement yet.'

Julie looked at him and then at Maggie in

bewilderment. 'Maggie hates to be called Red,' she finally said in her soft voice, her annoyance with Maggie replaced by astonishment.

Nick's lips curved in a brief grin. 'I know.'

'Are you really going to marry Maggie?' Julie wanted to know.

'Why not? Do you have a better idea?' Nick asked.

'No,' Maggie said hoarsely, finally finding her voice. Please. Don't let Nick want Julie.

'No?' Nick looked at her coolly, his brow raised in mocking interrogation.

'I mean, no, I hadn't made the announcement yet,' she said hastily. 'I-I thought I'd w-wait for you,' she stammered.

'Liar,' he said softly before smiling wryly at Julie. 'I think your sister had hopes that she could back out of our agreement.'

'Oh no, not Maggie,' Julie quickly defended her. 'If she says she'll do something, she will. You can always depend on her.'

'I didn't know you two knew each other,' Bayard said, nervously cracking his knuckles.

There's a lot of things you don't know,' Nick said, his icy voice cracking across the room like a whip.

'Nick and I met last year,' Maggie said hastily.

'That's true,' Nick drawled. 'She turned me down then, but today I made her an offer she couldn't refuse.'

Maggie's heart stopped in the middle of a beat. No mistaking the threat behind that remark.

'I think it's wonderful,' Julie said. 'Even if it is hard to believe that Maggie has been leading a secret life all this time. Imagine. Maggie getting married.' Her voice was full of wonder, conveying to the whole room that nothing short of a miracle could have brought about such an unlikely circumstance.

'What's so wonderful about it?' Bayard asked. 'Maggie doesn't look as if she thinks it's so great.'

Maggie looked at her brother in dismay. If Bayard discovered what she was doing . . . 'I . . . I have a headache, that's all.'

Nick frowned. 'I hope that's not a hint for me to leave.'

'No,' Maggie said quickly. Nick's friendly attitude towards Julie didn't fool her for one second. He was still angry and she had to placate him. For Bayard's sake. 'I know you want to make plans.'

'Let me get you an aspirin,' Julie said quickly. Returning with two tablets and a glass of water, she smiled beguilingly at Nick. 'I've always wanted to be at a big wedding. Don't you think I'd look smashing in an enormous pink cartwheel hat?' Hand on the back of her head, she posed for Nick.

He was sitting on the sofa beside Maggie, one had carelessly massaging the back of her neck. 'You're right,' he murmured to Maggie. 'The requisite swan-like neck.'

Maggie's spirits fell even further. Julie was lovely, with pale ash-blonde hair that floated around her sweet, heart-shaped face. In a charming aqua dress that matched her eyes, she was a magnet holding Nick's gaze. 'You know that I can't afford a big wedding,' Maggie said, more harshly than she intended.

'I know we can't,' Julie said, peering shyly at Nick from beneath lowered lashes. 'I thought that maybe Mr Ryan . . .' her voice trailed off wistfully. 'With the store and all . . .'

'You thought wrong,' Maggie said shortly.

Nick brushed her objection aside. 'I don't see why I shouldn't provide for the wedding. On two conditions, Julie.'

'What?' she asked eagerly.

'In the first place you have to stop calling me Mr Ryan. My name is Nick. And secondly, you have to promise to wear a dress just the colour of the one you're wearing now.'

'Nick.' She blushed prettily, before turning to Maggie. 'Isn't this going to be fun? I can just see the dress for you. Pure white and rows and rows and rows of ruffles. Carrying a bouquet of pink roses. It's so romantic,' she sighed.

The pounding behind Maggie's temples increased. 'We're not going to have a big wedding. We'll just run by a register office, or something.'

'I insist on a big church wedding, Red,' Nick said. 'A woman only gets married once.'

There it was again. The threat hidden behind a romantic remark. She couldn't argue about it in front of the family without disclosing the truth. 'All right,' she conceded ungraciously. 'We'll have a fancy wedding, but I'm paying for it. I can make our dresses.'

'I'm the man of the family. I'll pay for the wedding,' Bayard said challengingly.

Nick shifted so that his back was to Bayard. 'Maggie, don't be stubborn. Let me send you some dresses and pay for the wedding.'

Maggie looked from Nick's sardonic face to Bayard's, fiery red at Nick's casual rebuff. Couldn't Nick see that Bayard's offer was his way of trying to atone to Maggie for his behaviour? 'I'm sure that Bayard and I can manage the wedding expenses ourselves,' she said stiffly. Glancing at her sister's downcast face, she added, 'If you want to send Julie a dress, I guess that's between the two of you.'

Julie immediately proved where her loyalties lay. 'No, it's your wedding, Maggie, and if you want to make my dress, that's OK by me. Besides,' she added ingenuously, 'I do want to wear pink.'

Nick laughed. 'All right, Maggie wins.' He jerked his head towards the door. 'You two. Out. The future bridegroom wants to talk to his intended.'

Bayard quickly escaped. Julie, on the other hand, hesitated for a moment before throwing her arms around Nick and bestowing a big kiss on his cheek. 'Welcome to the family, Nick.' She ran from the room.

'Hard to believe that she's your sister,' Nick said after several long moments of silence.

'Because we look so different?'

'I wasn't thinking of looks so much as I was about how differently you behave. She's much less suspicious than you. And so innocent. I expected her to be older.'

'She's only eighteen,' Maggie said swiftly, inwardly hoping his remark meant he had realised that Julie was much too young for him.

'You mean she hasn't learned how to be a thief yet?'

'I only took a hundred dollars,' Maggie flushed. 'Would you have had me run out of petrol in the middle of New Mexico?'

'No, Red. I'd have had you ask me for the money.'

'Why are you doing this? You can't really want to marry me. After staying single all these years, why do you want to tie yourself down to a woman . . .'

'A woman I dislike?' He quickly finished the

question for her. 'Maybe because I'm tired of being a bachelor.'

'Even supposing that were true, there must be plenty of women in Colorado eager for . . . for this honour.' Her voice left no doubt what she thought about said honour.

'Possibly,' Nick agreed in silken tones. 'But there are certain advantages in selecting you. You see, I know that beneath that cold exterior is a stick of dynamite waiting to go off and I'm looking forward to lighting the fuse.'

'In that case, you'd better be careful or you'll burn yourself,' she swiftly retorted.

Nick chuckled, a heartless sound devoid of amusement. 'I don't think so, Red. You're the one in danger. You knew it then and you know it now. You ran before, but there'll be no running this time. A coward and a thief.' His eyes narrowed. 'Or was that maidenly shrinking all an act? Perhaps it was my money you were after all along?' He ignored her gasp. 'What a disappointment for you to find so little cash in my wallet.'

Pride wouldn't let her look away. 'If you think I'm such a criminal, why are you planning to marry me?'

'You made a mistake, Red, a very big mistake. You made me want you so badly, all I have to do is shut my eyes and I can taste your skin. Red-headed, hot-blooded thief that you are, I won't be denied having you in my bed.'

Maggie barely controlled a shiver at his words. 'If all you want is to satisfy your lust, there are plenty of motels in Tucson. We needn't go through with this farce of a marriage.'

'Oh no, Red. You left me with a hunger that is going to take a long time to appease.'

'And when you're tired of me, what then?' she cried.

He gave her a malevolent grin. 'I don't expect to get tired of you. It so happens that I have an incentive for you to to work very hard at keeping me a happy and satisfied husband. All the documentation proving your brother's thieving ways.' He paused. 'You were the one who said that getting married was exchanging one prison for another. As my wife, you'll find out just how prophetic that remark was.'

CHAPTER FIVE

IN keeping with her mood Maggie had hoped for rain
but the day of her wedding dawned hot and dry, the
bright July sun shining relentlessly down on the small
neighbourhood chapel where she was purchasing
Bayard's freedom with her own. Nick had initially
insisted that the wedding take place as soon as
possible but in the end he had agreed to Maggie's
request to finish her school duties. Even so, barely a
month had passed since Nick had explained clearly
and concisely to Maggie what her future held.

At first Bayard had wanted to discuss Nick and the
reason for the sudden wedding but Maggie, never
good at lying, had been evasive, so that Bayard,
blaming Maggie's erratic mood swings on premarital
jitters, soon began to avoid her. While Maggie was
saddened by the gulf opening between herself and her
brother, at the same time, she had to confess that in
her moments of darkest despair she came close to
hating Bayard for placing her in such a loathsome
situation. While she had repeatedly assured herself
that if Bayard knew of the sacrifices she was making
for him he would not allow it, deep down inside her
was the tiniest seed of fear that her brother was weak.

Maggie blamed herself for not developing
Bayard's spine. With no father to guide him and an
older sister who had firmly directed his every action,
Bayard had never had a chance to learn how to make
decisions. She should have allowed him more
freedom as a youngster so that when he decided

wrong and failed he could have learned from his failures. Instead, so intent on taking the place of the parents he had lost, so determined that he would be a success in life, she had never allowed him to be the man of the family. Was it any wonder that he had so weakly followed the path of least resistance? She had failed him by forcing him to lean on her too much. Abandoning him now when the consequences were so horrible would be terribly unfair to him. Nevertheless, his weakness was as bitter a pill to swallow as her marriage.

The rich, melodic sound of organ music filled the small church. In front of Maggie, Julie was quivering with anticipation. If the bride was less than radiant with happiness, the maid of honour was bubbling over with excitement. Julie had been too elated with the beautiful pink dress and matching cartwheel hat that had arrived in an elegant Ryan's box shortly after Nick's departure from Tucson even to consider that Maggie could be other than hopelessly in love with a man so wonderful. Maggie could see Nick standing at the altar, smiling warmly at Julie waiting at the rear of the church. Julie would be smiling back at him with adoration written all over her face. Maggie didn't doubt that her sister would be walking down the aisle in white if Nick hadn't decided that Julie was too young for him.

Nick. Registered Nicholas Peter Ryan. A name easily, and deceitfully, abbreviated. For protection from predatory women, he had smoothly told Maggie when she had asked him why he had lied to her at his cabin. She wondered what else he had lied about. Unfortunately, she would find out soon enough. At least he had had the decency to leave her alone this past month. The day after he had delivered his ultimatum they had taken the necessary tests and made all the necessary arrangements and then Nick had returned to Colorado, not arriving back in Tucson until the prenuptial dinner the previous evening. Surrounding herself with family and friends Maggie had managed to avoid being alone with him. A very small victory in view of her future.

As Julie started down the aisle, a glass door in the church vestibule reflected Maggie's image back to her. She was a turn-of-the-century bride in a dress that had been treasured and lovingly preserved to be handed down from generation to generation. Considering the circumstances under which she was getting married, Maggie had intended to make herself a modern bridal gown, but the nostalgic pull of the heirloom gown had proved too strong. And there was no denying that the dress suited her. The white lightweight cotton lawn had yellowed to a soft creamy colour that was especially flattering to Maggie with her pale ivory skin. A high neckline and rows of vertical tucking accentuatd her slim build, the simple lines of the dress decorated with inserts of Battenberg lace. There was no matching veil for the dress but she had found an old lace mantilla that had belonged to her mother and fastened it over hair knotted loosely atop her head.

Maggie thought of the wedding dress that Nick had sent to her. Snow-white and yards and yards and yards of ruffles. It might have been designed specifically for Julie. On Maggie it was a disaster. Her skin was sallow against the stark white of the fabric, while ruffles had never suited her personality. The dress had been returned with a curt note.

The organ music changed. Her cue. Placing her hand on Bayard's arm, Maggie started down the aisle. She had never had much time the past few years to daydream about getting married, merely expecting that she would have the same kind of marriage as her parents had had. There wasn't much money in the Russell household while Maggie was growing up, but there had always been an abundance of love and laughter. The groom had been a shadowy figure to whom she hadn't given much thought. She supposed that he would be tall and handsome . . . The march to the front of the church was endless. She risked a peep at Nick. He gave her a charming smile. Tentatively she smiled back. The she noticed his eyes. There was no smile there. Her future husband was coldly furious.

Maggied faltered in her stride. Nick stepped swiftly to her side. Afterwards she could remember nothing of the ceremony except for the low timbre of Nick's strong voice speaking the vows, the sun pouring through stained-glass windows in bands of colour, flickering candles and the overpowering scent of roses. Yellow roses from the bouquet that Nick had sent her. She wondered if she would ever again be able to smell roses without having this same sick feeling of dread.

The remainder of the day passed in a blurred series of surrealistic vignettes: being photographed in front of the church, her lips stretched in a gruesome imitation of a smile; enduring the travesty of a wedding reception with friends and neighbours brimming with joy for her and mounds of white-wrapped packages to be unwrapped and exclaimed over. Guests, caught up in the illusory romance of the occasion, spared her no bridal tradition—cutting the cake, toasts to the bridal couple, throwing the wedding bouquet, showers of rice. And through it all, Maggie was forced to smile and laugh and pretend that she was deeply in love and delirious with happiness, all the while uneasily aware of Nick, stiff and cold beside her. What's the matter with all of you? she wanted to scream. Can't you see I'm miserable? Are you all blind?

It was almost a relief to find herself alone with Nick. Saying goodbye to Julie and Bayard had been unbearably difficult. Julie had smiled bravely through her tears, but her hugs had been convulsive, and she had been almost belligerent in commanding Nick to take care of Maggie. Bayard had promised to watch out for Julie before awkwardly hugging Maggie. He had offered his hand to Nick even more awkwardly. Nick had shaken it after only a slight hesitation. Maggie tried to swallow the huge lump of homesickness that clogged her throat.

'Fasten your seat-belt,' Nick said brusquely beside her. The large plane that was to fly them back to Colorado was already starting to taxi out to the runway.

'I'm sorry that none of your family could make it to the wedding,' she said nervously, dutifully snapping the belt across her lap. 'Your mother called to apologise for the fact that your father's health didn't permit them to travel from California at this time. She also explained about your sister's trip to Europe. She was so pleasant. I . . . I feel like a fraud.' Her words fell into a pool of icy silence. 'I guess that you didn't tell her the truth about our marriage.'

'Very perceptive,' Nick snapped.

'Why . . . why not?'

'You didn't tell Julie and your brother the truth, did you?'

'No.' She turned to look out of the window.

'I didn't think so. Julie is too transparent to hide her feelings and she was obviously thrilled about the whole affair. As for your brother, even he should have shown some remorse. All I saw was relief. Why didn't you tell them?'

For fear that Julie would insist on taking her place, Maggie thought, but out loud she only said, 'I saw no reason to.'

'No reason? You're going to the stake for your brother and you don't even bother to tell him of your sacrifice?'

'You know nothing about it,' she cried. 'Bayard would never have allowed the wedding to take place if he'd known the truth.'

'Are you so sure of that?'

'Yes,' she said defiantly, as much to slay her own doubts as Nick's.

'Or perhaps you were afraid to put his brotherly affections to the test?'

Maggie stared sightlessly out the window. 'That's an . . . an ugly . . . awful . . . hurtful thing to say,' she said unevenly.

'The truth always hurts,' Nick said brutally. 'You haven't saved your brother from anything by marrying me. He'll just go out and do the same thing again. And how will you save him then? You should have let him face the consequences this time.'

Maggie shook her head wearily. 'You're wrong. Bayard does know that what he did was wrong, even if somewhere along the way I failed to give him the proper moral guidance. Maybe when Nana was sick. Or maybe I gave Julie too much of my time.' She sighed wearily. 'Whatever the reason, I couldn't abandon him when he needed me most. He depended on me. Besides, if it hadn't been for me . . .' Her voice trailed off.

'You can't blame yourself.'

'Yes, I can. None of this would have happened if I hadn't recklessly rushed off to Aspen on an impulse. I . . . I wouldn't be married to . . . to you.'

'I'm curious about that trip. It seems so out of character for you. Julie, your neighbours—everyone —has depicted you as a woman who is all work and no play. Dependable. Never a rash moment. Never an impulsive decision.'

'Labels,' Maggie said with loathing. 'Maggie the dependable. Maggie the responsible. No one ever said Maggie the fun-loving or Maggie the fascinating. Just one time I wanted to be someone else. I was so tired of my life. Dull. Boring. Heading to Aspen on a whim didn't seem so dangerous in the beginning. But then . . . I met you. You were the first man who . . .' she swallowed. 'You didn't treat me as if I was dull and boring. You acted as if . . . as if I was exciting. I knew it wasn't true, knew it couldn't last, but I . . . I liked your kisses. A daring Maggie appeared from out of nowhere and urged me to take advantage of the anonymity of the situation, to be spontaneous for once in my life. Who would ever know? I thought I could until I remembered Julie. Even if she never found out what I'd done, I owed it to her to be as responsible as I'm always nagging at her to be. You see,' her voice caught momentarily, 'I thought that I could ignore dull old Maggie, but she's too ingrained in me.'

'I suppose that the daring Maggie rifled my wallet and stole the money and the dull one left the note.'

She could feel the colour warm her face. 'If I hadn't done that, you wouldn't have been so angry.

Bayard's first offence—he might have been fired, but not threatened with prison. You wanted to hurt me, and Bayard's theft gave you the perfect excuse. You didn't care about punishing me.'

'I don't like thieves, Red.'

'That's not it at all,' she said slowly. 'It's not the money you're mad about. You're mad because I ran out on you—rejected you.'

'I've handled plenty of rejections in my time,' he said caustically. 'It was the way you did it. Stealing off in the middle of the night as if you were afraid I'd sneak into the bedroom and rape you. Saying no in a big way is a trademark of yours, isn't it? Like with the wedding dress.' He paused, but she made no comment. 'Julie wrote me a nice thank-you note for her dress.' He waited again. 'She was a fresh and lovely rose coming down the aisle today, while you . . .'

'While I was the faded autumn leaf,' Maggie bit out.

'While you looked tired. Circles under your eyes. I'll bet you've lost ten pounds since I saw you last. Why wouldn't you wear the dress I sent you? Stiff-necked pride? I thought every woman wanted to look her best on her wedding day. You wouldn't catch Julie refusing to wear an expensive dress like the one I sent. Why did you?'

'Because it looked like hell on me,' Maggie flashed. 'What did you do? Call up your store and describe Julie? Couldn't you even remember what your intended bride looked like? A blind man could have seen I'd look hideous in that . . . that ruffled monstrosity.'

Nick gave her a scorching look. 'And since I'm not blind, you concluded that I deliberately sent you an unflattering dress, is that it? Did if ever occur to you that I selected that particular dress because Julie said it would be perfect for you?'

'No.'

'If you didn't like that dress, I could have sent you another one.'

'Another one designed for a cute little blonde? No, thank you.'

Nick stared at her, an arrested look on his face. 'You were insulted by the dress being so unsuitable. That's why you dug up that old rag you wore. I could have wrung your neck when I saw you walking down the aisle. Ryan's entire chain at your disposal and you had to shop the local rummage sales.'

'Old rag!' Maggied glared at him. 'I'll have you know that my mother, my grandmother, and my great-grandmother were all married in that dress. My mother said wearing that dress brought luck to a bride, that it was a symbol of love and hope and a belief in the holy sanctity of marriage. By wearing it today, I probably put a curse on it,' she added bitterly, turning her face to the window. Below them a range of mountains thrust jagged peaks up from the undulating landscape, evidence of the tumultuous happenings that had taken place thousands of years ago.

Nick accepted a newspaper from the air hostess. 'You haven't come off so badly. A new house, a husband most women would find acceptable, an entire department-store chain at your fingertips.' A sarcastic note crept into his voice. 'Not to mention no more lonely nights for you. I haven't forgotten how much you enjoyed being in my arms.'

Her head whipped around. 'You're wrong,' she said fiercely. 'I hated it. Why do you think I ran out on you?'

'You tell me. Why did you?'

'You said it yourself. A strange man. A lonely cabin in the woods. And no one knew where I was. Naturally I wanted to . . . to escape at the first possible moment,' she lied. 'Everything else was . . . I wanted to humour you . . . just a front . . . I didn't want you to get mad. How did I know that you weren't a murderer or rapist?'

Nick laughed without humour. 'Liar. I knew when you were afraid of me and I knew when you stopped being afraid. I never forced myself on you up at the cabin.'

Maggie plucked at the seat-belt buckle with nervous fingers. 'I never said you did,' she admitted in a low voice.

'So don't bother to look to me for sympathy now,' he added in a harsh voice.

'I wouldn't think of it,' she flashed.

'Why should you?' He snapped the newspaper open. 'If you'd stayed in Tucson you would have been so busy taking care of your brother and sister that before you knew what had happened they'd have been married and leaving their runny-nosed brats with you and you'd never have broken free.'

'I'm not free now. I'm married.'

'So am I, Red,' he said wearily. 'So am I.' Folding the paper to the business section, he began to read.

Maggie stared incredulously at Nick's bent head. That last remark sounded as if Nick was regretting their marriage. Could it be that he was only now realising that if their marriage was a prison for Maggie, it was no less confining for him? There was a world out there full of beautiful women like Julie, no doubt his for the asking. Instead, he was stuck with

Maggie. How the gods must be laughing at him. If only she could laugh with them.

'Nick,' she began hesitantly. 'Why did you really marry me?'

For a moment she thought he hadn't heard her, but then he laid down the paper and looked at her. 'Why do you think?'

'I know you were angry . . .'

'Angry?' he interrupted. 'When you walked into that office I wanted to wring your neck.'

'Not a very good foundation for marriage,' Maggie pointed out. She traced the flower pattern in her skirt with an unsteady finger. 'Are you still angry with me?'

'Why didn't you tell me to go to hell when I made that stupid proposal?' he countered. 'You showed more gumption up at the cabin.'

'You're blaming me for this marriage?' Maggie asked heatedly. 'I didn't threaten someone you love with prison.'

'Do you mean to sit there and tell me you believed that I would actually carry out that threat?'

'Of course I did. Why do you think I married you?'

'Why indeed?' Nick said enigmatically. He gave a short snort of laughter. 'Rather hard on the ego to know that a woman has to be forced to be my wife.'

'It's not too late to call it off,' Maggie suggested.

'The hell it isn't. And why should we anyway? What's the problem with staying married? You escape your humdrum life and I have the little woman to welcome me home after a hard day's work.'

'What about love?'

'Love,' he snorted. 'A vastly overrated

commodity. Most of my friends married for love. Most of them divorced because they couldn't stand their spouses.'

'That's a very cynical point of view.'

'Realistic. The man sees a beautiful blonde, the woman sees a strong back. After a couple of weeks of marriage he realises that she wants to go dancing every night and he hates dancing. She realises that he snores and it drives her crazy. Before you know it—wham—divorce court.'

'You snore,' Maggie said.

'And you already knew it. No surprises.'

'This is crazy. I can't believe we're discussing it. The sensible thing is for us to admit here and now that we made a mistake and dissolve this marriage before it goes any further.'

'And you're always sensible, is that it?'

'You don't need to say it as if it's some kind of despicable flaw in my personality.'

'Isn't it?' he taunted her. 'I thought you were the one who said you hated always being thought of as sensible. Isn't that how you ended up in my cabin in the first place?'

'And look what happened,' she said bitterly.

'What happened? You ran out before anything could.'

Maggie could feel the red stinging her cheeks. 'You know what I mean. This. Us. Being married.'

Nick took one of her hands and played with the fingers. 'Let's look at this marriage for a minute. When you really think about it, it is sensible. No, let me finish,' he forestalled her interruption. 'Forget your blasted pride for a minute and admit that you're better off financially as my wife. You've been carrying too big a load for too long a time. You need my help.'

She wrenched her hand from his grasp. 'I do not. I've managed perfectly well without you for years.'

'Bayard is the perfect example of that.'

Maggie paled. 'That's a low blow.'

'It's the truth. What would have happened to your brother if I hadn't been there when his little crimes came to light? As far as that goes, where would you be today if I hadn't come looking for you that night in the snow?'

There was no denying the truth of what Nick was saying. Maggie was obliged to him. But marriage? 'But what do you get out of our marriage? I . . . I don't love you.'

'I know that. The truth is, I'm tired of all this bachelor business. I suppose that I could go out and find myself a wife easily enough, but another woman would want romance and to be courted and all that stuff. After we got married, she'd expect me to be on time to dinner and hang around her at parties and not flirt with other women and want me to spend all my spare time with her. I don't want a woman who clings or demands to own me, body and soul. At least you're sensible. When I'm busy, you'll go off and read a book. And if I flirt, why should you care? You've admitted tht you're not in love with me.'

'It's crazy even to think about it,' Maggie said rather faintly.

'No. What's crazy is your rejecting this proposal. You haven't come up with one sensible idea against it. Besides,' he shuddered dramatically, 'I can't go through the fuss of getting married again. All those giggling, inquisitive women in the store. You'd have thought that my marriage was the most important event in their lives.' He reached for Maggie's hand

and raised it to his lips, pressing a soft kiss in her palm. Persuasive blue eyes met troubled turquiose ones. 'Won't you spare me having to go through that again, Red?'

Maggie felt her stomach lurch. The plane must have hit an air-pocket. She shook her head, trying to break the spell of Nick's compelling gaze. What he wanted from her was wrong, crazy. She couldn't do it. So whose was the voice she heard agreeing?

She was still wondering several hours later as she looked distractedly around the large bedroom to which Nick had directed her. Modern, high-tech furniture with lots of dark leather and chrome and impossible curves, a large black metal wood-burning stove, cool in July, and metallic thin-slatted mini-blinds covered the large windows. On the floor an enormous black and white cowhide was the sole approximation to a rug. Maggie wrinkled her nose in distaste. A set of french doors beckoned, and she walked across the enormous room, her high heels clicking loudly on the pale, pickled-wood floor. The doors led to a veranda, beyond which the black night was penetrated by only a few lonely stars. Vaguely chilled, Maggie turned away.

The only spot of colour in the room was a flame-coloured mohair throw tossed across the bottom of the bed. The bed. Maggie could no longer avoid looking at it. A spare Shaker four-poster painted a deep forest green and piled high with creamy eyelet lace and embroidered linens, it dominated the room. Gingerly Maggie sat down on the bed's edge. It moved beneath her. Startled, she jumped up. A water bed.

Facing the end of the bed, an elaborately tooled silver-framed mirror reflected her image. The strain of the past month and the long day had etched itself on her face. No wonder Nick had unfavourably compared her appearance with Julie's. Her eyes were deep smudges set in skin pale with weariness. Here and there tendrils of red had escaped the pinned-up mass of hair and the rest suddenly seemed too heavy a burden for her slender neck and abominably aching head to bear.

She turned away from the relentless honesty of the mirror. They had landed in Denver and taken a taxi to a small restaurant where they had eaten dinner while waiting for Nick's car and driver to pick them up. The dark limousine had nosed its way through Denver traffic before heading west on the turnpike to Boulder. In the fast-fading twilight she had only managed to make out the barest outlines of jagged mountains before they had come into city traffic again. There were stops and turns and always a sense of climbing before the car had swept into a driveway. Maggie had caught only a glimpse of a large wooden house before Nick had led her inside.

Tomorrow she would investigate her new home. Tonight . . . When she had agreed to stay married to Nick fulfilling his requirements for a wife hadn't seemed so difficult: talk when he wanted and shut up when he didn't. She had never once considered the physical side of marriage. Little as she knew of Nick, she knew that he would expect her to share his bed. A desolate sense of longing swept over her. Other brides on their wedding night looked forward to an act that was the ultimate in trust and giving—the most beautiful expression of their shared love. A sharp stab of envy pierced Maggie's heart. Without love, her and Nick's coupling would be no more than satisfying desires. Unbidden, memories of their kisses came to her. Was it just her imagination or could she hear her heart pounding, the loud sound echoing off the glossy white walls?

Nick had tossed her luggage through a connecting door with the briefest of explanations that it was a dressing-area before going downstairs to check his mail and messages. Maggie crossed the room, her heels again clicking out a message of loneliness. Swiftly she bent over and removed them, padding on nylon-clad feet to the open doorway. In no time at all she had shaken out the few garments she had brought and hung them up in the huge closet. Even when the rest of her things arrived she wouldn't be able to fill half that space. Peeking into the bedroom and seeing no sign yet of Nick, Maggie decided to take a quick shower.

Back out of the shower and towelled off, she grabbed her old cotton shift and slid it over her head. Hardly glamorous, but the high cost of the wedding had precluded her buying anything resembling a trousseau.

Returning to the bedroom she slid gingerly between the soft sheets, fighting tidal waves that threatened to eject her. At last they subsided and Maggie lay trembling on one side of the huge bed. Her eyes wandered around the room, coming back to rest on an odd smudge over her head. She twisted her body around to get a better look. There was a large oblong shape on the wall that was somehow different from the rest of the wall. Almost as if a picture had been hanging there. Maggie fell asleep wondering what the picture had been and why Nick had removed it.

When she opened her eyes the sun was doing its best to invade the room from between the thin slats of the blinds. Too bright. She closed her eyes again and then suddenly popped them open in shock. She was alone in the enormous bed. Wildly she looked around. Alone in the enormous room. Several dark hairs resting in the deep indentation of the pillow beside hers gave evidence that Nick had spent the night beside her. Why hadn't he woken her? Something tugged at her consciousness, something in the room that hadn't been there last night. Slowly she studied the room, her eyes roving past the stove, the chairs, the table . . . There. On the table.

Forgetting that she was in a water bed, Maggie abruptly sat up. The next few seconds were a struggle to get out of a bed that seemed as determined to keep her in this morning as it had been to keep her out last night. At last, victorious, she tiptoed across the room, as if afraid that the slightest noise might make what she had seen disappear.

Resting on the dark enamelled surface of the table was a large silver tray. On the tray was a silver ice-bucket that contained a large bottle awash in water. Tentatively Maggie dipped her finger into the water. It was very cold. Melted ice. The label on the bottle grabbed her attention and she caught her breath. Champagne. And a very famous brand. A cork lying on the table and two glasses, one clean, the other bearing a few drops of liquid, told their own story. She had fallen asleep and Nick had celebrated their marriage in the traditional way—except that he had celebrated alone.

He could have woken her, she thought defensively. Apparently she had been wrong in thinking that Nick would expect her to be a wife in every sense of the word. It certainly appeared that he had no raging desire for her body.

Or her company. Dressed in a cool periwinkle-blue jumpsuit Maggie came downstairs to discover that she was alone in the empty house. A note in large, firm handwriting lay on a table in the kitchen. If she closed her eyes she could see Nick signing the marriage licence, a few dark hairs on the back of his hand as he firmly grasped the pen. She shook her head to erase the vision and read the note. He had gone to work and would be back some time this afternoon. There was food in the refrigerator. A single initial 'N' finished the note. Maggie swallowed hard. What did you expect? she jeered at herself. Hadn't he made it very plain that he wanted a wife who didn't interfere with his business? Or his pleasures.

By four o'clock Maggie had investigated every inch of Nick's house and detested it thoroughly. It was as stark and barren as the bedroom. The only exception was Nick's study. The door to the room had been closed, but Maggie peeped inside. There was leather here too, but it was the old leather of family heirlooms, while a deep red oriental rug and rows and rows of books warmed the room. Unfortunately, those appeared to be the only books in the house, and Maggie, unused to having time on her hands, had decided that, private or not, she was going to invade Nick's study for something to read. She had eaten several times, the moutain air giving her an appetite. She had sat on the veranda outside the bedroom and followed the progress of a couple of deer on the hillside behind the house with the aid of some binoculars that she had found on the table. She had even taken a nap, something that she had seldom done since she had been a small child. But enough was enough, she said huffily to herself. Her hand was on the handle of the study door when she heard footsteps. She whirled about.

Nick was coming down the hall, tugging at his tie. 'Well. If it isn't Sleeping Beauty.'

Maggie snatched back her hand as if the door handle were a burning brand.

He looked from her to the closed door and raised an inquisitive brow.

'I . . . I was just . . . I mean . . . a book . . . something to read . . .' Her voice trailed guiltily away.

'Is that all? I thought sure I'd caught you stealing the family silver.'

She flushed at the teasing note in his voice. 'I . . . I didn't want you to think that I was snooping, or, or anything,' she finished lamely.

Nick brushed past her, shoving open the door and flinging his briefcase on to the desk. 'Come in any time you want. I don't have any secrets.' Putting a stack of mail on the table, he thumbed through it.

Maggie stood akwardly in the doorway wishing that Nick would give her some clue as to what he expected from her. Being a librarian in a high school and dealing with male adolescent egos and personalities had done nothing to prepare her for dealing with this man. Was he angry about last night? Maybe she should apologise. No. He could have woken her.

She tried to quell the feeling of irritation that pricked at her. After abandoning her all day, did he intend to ingore her now, too? His words came back to her. He wanted a wife who would go and read a book when he was busy. All right. She would. Disregarding her pounding heart, she walked firmly to the bookcase and began studying the titles lined up on the shelves.

Her first clue that Nick had moved to stand behind
her was when he started removing the pins holding
her red hair secure at the nape of her neck.

'I trust you slept well last night.' There was no
mistaking the undercurrent of amusement in his
voice.

'Yes. Thank you.' She tried to keep her voice cool.

His thumbs casually kneaded her shoulders. 'And
I hope you appreciated my letting you sleep late this
morning.'

'Yes. Of course I did.' His hands slid down her
shoulders and his fingers began toying with the
buttons down the front of her jumpsuit. She
abandoned her search for a book and gripped the
edge of the bookshelves for support. Nick edged
closer behind her, the front of his body pressing
against her back. She breathed deeply, inhaling his
intoxicating male scent.

'Did you?' he murmured against the nape of her
neck, his lips warm on her skin. 'Or were you
disappointed?' he asked smoothly, his hands moving
inside her top.

'Why would I be disappointed?' She fought her
voice's tendency to wobble.

'I was. A bridegroom rather expects to find his
bride eagerly awaiting him.' He dealt decisively with
the lacy wisp of fabric that inadequately covered
breasts already swelling with anticipation.

'Why didn't you wake me up?' she breathed.

He ignored her question. 'The nightgown was a
nice touch.' Warm hands edged the jumpsuit off her
shoulders and down to her waist. White lace fell to
the floor.

'What do you mean?' She could scarcely breathe,

much less think.

A soft, derisive laugh greeted her question. 'Are you going to tell me that your nightgown was handed down from your great-grandmother to bless the nuptials?' Threading his fingers through her hair, he elected a long, wavy curl and brushed it across her shoulder and down her chest. With short, feathering strokes he teased a rosy nipple until it was taut with longing.

'No . . . no.'

'I didn't think so.' He gave a low, amused laugh.

'I couldn't afford a new nightgown, what with the cost of the wedding and all.' She nervously rattled off the explanation.

'The hell you couldn't. I'm surprised that you didn't sew a few patches on it to really rub it in.'

Maggie jerked her hair out of his hand and flung it back over her shoulder. 'Rub what in?'

'That I forced poor little you to marry me. Was I supposed to feel remorse when I saw how pathetic you looked?'

'Of course not,' Maggie said, uneasily aware that she could have found the money for a new nightgown if she had wanted to. Was Nick right? Had she deliberately worn the old one out of perversity?

He recaptured a hank of her hair and wrapped it around his fist, forcing her head around to face him. His lips hovered tantalisingly close to hers. 'Of course note,' he repeated in silken tones. 'I forgot for a minute who we were talking about here. Dull, respectable Maggie. No sexy lingerie for her. Naturally she'd wear something dull and respectable. Isn't that what all prim and proper librarians wear?' There was a challenge in his taunting voice.

Maggie flushed with anger at his words. Dull,

respectable Maggie. Something snapped within her. Stepping nimbly out of his grasp, she started unbuttoning the buttons he had left. 'I wouldn't know what prim and proper librarians wear,' she said icily. With a shrug of her body, the jumpsuit fell to the floor. She kicked it aside, a blue puddle on the rug. Bending over, she removed her sandals. Silkin underpanties went the same way as her jumpsuit. Stark naked, she walked to the door, and turned to face him, hands on her hips. 'If you're interested, I'll be in the bedroom.' Her courage fleeing before the dark, smouldering look in his eyes, she turned and fled up the stairs.

He followed more leisurely so that she was already in bed, the covers pulled up to her shoulders, by the time he entered the room. Walking over to the bed, he said softly, 'I'm interested.' Carefully he removed his clothing, slowly emptying his pockets, placing his shoes and socks precisely on the floor, folding his trousers meticulously along the crease before laying them across the chair, unbuttoning his shirt with agonising lack of speed. His chest muscles flexed as he eased out of the shirt with tantalising slowness, draping it carefully over his trousers. All the while his eyes were fixed on Maggie and she trembled beneath the covers, unable to look away. The slower he moved, the faster she breathed. Maggie could feel her entire body suffused with warm colour as Nick deliberately stuck his thumbs in his narrow briefs and slowly edged them down his body. Swallowing hard at the sight of all that flagrant masculinity, she made herself slowly scan his body from head to toe. 'Very nice.' To her relief, there was little evidence of her tumultuous emotions in her cool, approving voice.

With a short laugh, Nick swept the covers from her

body. 'That's what I like about you, Red. You're gutsy, damned gutsy.'

The bed gave a heave as he joined her but Maggie paid little heed to the motion as her senses were bombarded with the evidence of his physical presence. The curly hair on his chest tormented her sensitive breasts while the curious combination of maleness and aftershave that was his alone filled her nostrils. She drank of the sweet taste of his mouth before her tongue lapped along the inside curve of his shoulder licking the salt from his skin. Her breathing quickened as his hands moved downwards on a path of exploration and her body tensed nervously in anticipation.

Later Maggie lay barely moving, her breathing slowly returning to normal. Nick was silent beside her, his hip warm against hers. Over the past few months it had frequently occurred to her that she had probably romanticised their encounter, making it more exciting than it had actually been. But if anything, the reverse was true. Their marriage was definitely unconventional, but Maggie couldn't deny the wonderful and glorious passion that Nick sparked within her. She wished she knew if he had been as pleased by her.

Nick stirred at her side. 'Who was he?' he asked in a cold voice.

CHAPTER SIX

'WHO was who?' Maggie asked drowsily.

'Don't be coy with me. You know who I mean. The man you've been with.' Nick rolled out of bed and stalked into the dressing-room, leaving Maggie fighting the bed and staring after him in astonishment.

'I was a virgin. Surely you could tell that.'

'A technical virgin is, I believe, what it's called,' he sneered.

'I don't think I know what that is,' she said in uncertainty.

Nick reappeared in the doorway belting a burgundy kimono-style robe around his waist. 'A woman who's done everything except go all the way. Your level of expertise in the art of making love has increased dramatically since last we met. I'm curious as to the identity of your tutor. He's to be congratulated on the success of his pupil. But then, I noticed before that you were a quick learner.'

Maggie swallowed the nervous giggle that bubbled up in her throat. One minute Nick called her dull and respectable; the next he accused her of being a red-haired temptress. When did he think she had the time to be hopping in and out of men's arms? Not that it was any of his business if she had been. And so she informed him.

'I'm your husband. Naturally it's my business to know who you're kissing.' He leaned against the door-jamb, his hands thrust into the robe's pockets.

'Present tense—I'm kissing you. Past tense is not your business. Just because I forgot myself with you seven months ago, was I supposed to save myself the rest of my life, just in case we ran into each other again?'

'You saved yourself for twenty-four years before you met me, didn't you? Another few months of abstinence wouldn't have hurt you.'

Maggie braved the rolling bed to sit up, hugging a pillow to her chest. Peering beneath lowered lashes, she asked with false sweetness. 'Did it hurt you?'

'No.'

The curt answer took Maggie's breath away. 'Are you telling me that you haven't . . . that between then and now . . . that I'm . . .?' Her voice trailed off in disbelief.

'What's the matter? You think that women have the lock on moral behaviour? Or did you assume that I spent my nights tom-catting down back alleys?'

'Why haven't you?'

'Been tom-catting?' he asked with a sarcastic twist of his mouth.

She brushed aside that answer. 'Why haven't you made love to another woman?'

'Maybe because I know how little the act of making love means to a woman,' he ground out before turning on his heel and disappearing back into the dressing-room.

Maggie felt as if she had been slapped. She scrambled out of bed and into her robe and followed him into the dressing-room. 'Oh you do, do you?' she asked furiously. 'Correct me if I'm wrong, but aren't you the man who forced me into his marriage bed by threatening to imprison my brother? Aren't you the man who claims that love is fleeting and overrated? What do you know about the act of making love?'

'Obviously not as much as the man who was able to increase your sexual education to such a surprising degree.' He uttered a sharp laugh. 'It's ungrateful of me to complain when I'm reaping the benefits of his very satisfactory training. Who was he?' he repeated.

'He?' Maggie echoed, her eyes glittering with anger. 'You think that I was content to learn from one man? There were dozens.'

The stark silence that met her claim was broken by the explosive crash of a hairbrush hitting the wall. She jumped. Nick slumped over the cabinets staring blindly at his whitened knuckles. 'It's my fault. I knew how innocent you were. I shouldn't have touched you at the cabin.' He turned and traced a shaky finger along her cheekbone. 'I'm sorry.'

There was no doubt about his sincerity and Maggie was immediately ashamed of herself. In her anger at his rash assumption, she had deliberately misled him. He had been in the wrong, but that didn't excuse her behaviour, although maybe he did deserve to be punished a little for jumping to such an unflattering conclusion. She peered up at him from beneath lowered lashes. 'You were the one who said that I was supposed to work very hard at keeping you a satisfied husband. I didn't think that I had enough—uh—knowledge to satisfy you very long, so naturally, being a librarian, I had to do some research.'

'Are you telling me that you went to other men to find out how to make me happy in bed? Didn't it ever occur to your silly red head to ask me what would satisfy me?'

'And not just men. Women, too.'

His eyes were black slits as he stared down at her. 'You're lying. You'd never—not with a woman.'

'Why not a woman? Women know about making love, too.' Immediately she saw from the icy anger on his face that she had gone too far. 'I told you, I'm a librarian. I did what all librarians do when they want to know something. They read a book.'

'A book? You read a book on making love?'

'Not one book. Lots of books. Some written by men and others written by women. Yo'd be amazed at how many books there are in the library on keeping a husband happy in bed.'

'How-to books on making love?' Nick repeated.

'Why not? There are books on how to do about everything else. You just have to know where to look.'

'Then you haven't been experimenting with another man?'

'You're quick to grasp a point. Almost as quick as you are at jumping to nasty conclusions.'

His lips twisted in a wry grin. 'That's what I like about you, Red. You may not have a swan-like neck, but you always come out slugging.'

'Most husbands wouldn't consider that an asset to a marriage,' she said.

'But then, I'm not most husbands, am I?'

You certainly aren't, Maggie thought later as she sat in the kitchen sipping a glass of wine while Nick tossed a salad for dinner. He had refused her help, insisting she needed her rest after the rigours of planning their wedding. And Maggie had to admit he was more than competent in the kitchen. Potatoes cooked in the microwave oven while an enormous steak lay waiting on the cabinet. The red cotton sweater and blue jeans he sported might not be usual culinary attire, but few women would object to such a darkly handsome chef. A day's growth of beard darkened his face. Idly she wondered how he managed to shave that deep cleft in his chin.

'What do you think of the house?' Nick was watching her as he sprinkled seasoning over the greens.

'It's certainly different from what I'm used to. So big and modern. And to be honest, rather quiet and empty. I'm used to more noise. Julie and Bayard hollering around the house with their friends. To think I used to complain about the sound of the televison.' She ran her finger aimlessly around the rim of her glass. 'I even miss Archie's barking.'

'You're the one who decided to leave him in Tucson,' Nick reminded her.

'I know. It was the right decision. He'll be protection for Julie when she's alone.'

'I don't think she'll be alone much,' Nick said drily.

'What do you mean?'

'Julie was born knowing how to attract men even if she is only beginning to realise it. She's like a beautiful butterfly and scores of men will be pursuing her, each hoping to be the lucky one who captures her.'

Maggie's heart plummeted to her toes. She had almost forgotten that Nick had fallen for Julie's photograph on Bayard's desk. 'You seem to have given it a great deal of thought,' she said, her calm voice denying how much Nick's words upset her.

Nick set the sizzling steak on the table. 'It fascinates me how two women in the same family can be so different.'

'I've never pretended to be a butterfly,' Maggie

said stiffly.

Nick brought over the potatoes. 'No. You're more like a honey-bee. Hard-working. Dependable.' Passing behind her, he tugged sharply on a dangling curl. 'And like a bee, you've got a sting in your tail.'

'I suppose that's a reference to my temper,' she said, thrusting away the hurt at the unfavourable comparison of her with Julie.

If Nick heard her question, he ignored it. Instead he turned the coversation to telling Maggie about his day.

After dinner he went into his office saying he had some paperwork. Maggie noticed that her need to rest didn't excuse her from washing up the dishes, not that there was nuch to do since Nick had the latest in dishwashers installed in his kitchen. Once the kitchen was cleaned up she wandered around the house, the barren-looking furniture mocking her solitary figure. At last, driven by loneliness, she ventured into Nick's office. He looked up and smiled abstractedly at her before returning to his papers. Feeling at least that she wasn't unwelcome, Maggie selected a book about Colorado from his well-stocked shelves and curled up in a worn, leather chair.

The bag tossed into her lap brought Maggie back from the goldfields of Cripple Creek. 'What's this?' She looked up to see Nick leaning back in his chair across the room watching her, his hands crossed behind his head.

'Open it and find out.'

The Ryan's logo jumped out at her as Maggie gingerly picked up the bag. Reaching into it, she pulled out the contents. A silken peach-coloured nightgown cascaded into her lap. 'Oh, Nick. It's lovely,' she crooned, rubbing the soft fabric against her cheek. 'Thank you.'

'I didn't want to take the chance of damaging some family heirloom,' he said, a teasing light in his eyes.

Maggie blushed at his less-than-subtle reference to her old nightgown. She refused to allow him to put her on the defensive. 'Since you were good enough to buy this for me, I suppose that I ought to model it for you.'

'If you wouldn't mind.'

'I know my duty,' she said as she stood up and started for the door.

Nick moved around his desk and stood in the doorway. 'It sounds to me as if your hours in the library doing research were well spent.' He cupped a hand around her chin and lightly brushed her cheek with his thumb. 'Can I be of any help?'

Maggie felt herself drowning in fathomless blue eyes. 'I . . . I hear that you're very good with buttons . . . and . . . and stuff.'

'Very good.' Nick lowered his head.

The phone rang.

Nick grimaced. 'I'll be up as soon as I can. Try on the gown.'

'All right.' Dismissed, Maggie headed disconsolately up the stairs, the nightgown draped over her arm. Darn the phone.

Upstairs she dawdled for what seemed an eternity, but there was no sign of Nick. She couldn't put off trying on the nightgown any longer. Already lost was the spontaneity of the moment downstairs when Nick had made her feel so desirable. Stripping off her clothes, she picked up the nightgown and slid it over her head, glorying in the cool, silken feel of the satin charmeuse fabric as it slithered down her heated body. A tremendous rush of disappointment hit her as she gazed in the mirror. Despite the fabric, the nightgown could be classified as nothing less than respectable. A tube of warm peach fell to the floor, barely touching her body at strategic points while lace sleeves modestly covered her freckled shoulders. Nick couldn't have made his opinion of her clearer if he had shouted it to the entire world. Dowdy, sexless, dull.

'Maggie,' Nick's voice hollered up the staircase. 'Julie is on the phone.'

Maggie's spirits dropped further. He had been on the phone to Julie all this time. Was that why he had been in no hurry to terminate the conversation and come upstairs to the bedroom where his plain, sensible wife waited?

The extension was beside the bed. 'Maggie, I'm sorry to bother you,' Julie's voice came blithely over the wires, 'but Bayard's not at home and I can't remember how to set the video and there's a super movie on tonight that I want to tape.'

Hurt by the implications of Nick's gift, Maggie's voice was sharper than she intended. 'Then why didn't you call a neighbour?' The injured silence that came over the telephone wire sent a flood of remorse over Maggie. It wasn't Julie's fault that Nick preferred her conversation to Maggie's company.

Besides, she was perfectly aware that Julie's call was prompted by loneliness. Gratitude that at least Julie loved her washed over her as she patiently explained the mysterious workings of the video. Remembering the scene that Julie had interrupted she added hesitantly, 'And Julie, in the future, please remember that Nick and I are on our honeymoon and lay off the phone calls for awhile, OK?

The sound of a sniff was clear. 'Nick said to call if I had any problems or in an emergency.'

'Do you really think this was an emergency tonight?'

There was a long pause. 'No,' Julie admitted.

'I still love you and Bayard, even if I did get married,' Maggie explained. 'But the first few weeks of a marriage—learning to live with a stranger—it takes work.'

'What's it like being married?' Julie asked eagerly. 'Nick is so handsome. I want to marry a man just like him. Do you live in a mansion and have lots of servants to do everything?'

'You'd hate it. They even draw my bath and cut up my meat. You have no idea how dreary and boring it is being wealthy and having people wait on you hand and foot,' Maggie said solemnly.

'Makes you long for a nice, filthy oven to clean, I'll bet,' Julie teased.

'It's not that dreary and boring,' Maggie retorted. Julie laughed and the phone call ended on an upbeat note. Maggie replaced the receiver with a slight smile. Julie simply needed time to adjust to life without her elder sister. Maggie's marriage was as big an adjustment to her brother and sister as it was to her.

When Nick came into the bedroom Maggie waited for him to comment on the nightgown, but she soon discovered that Nick's thoughts were on an entirely different subject as he reached up and turned out the bedside lights. 'When are you ever going to treat Julie like a grown woman?' he asked.

The anger in his voice caught Maggie unaware and she gaped at him in the darkness. 'She's still a child,' she said defensively.

'She's eighteen. Old enough to lead her own life. Let her trip over her own mistakes.'

'And who will catch her when she falls? Bayard?' she asked bitterly.

'You've tied her to your apron-strings for years. So what are you going to do now? Tie her to you with long-distance telephone wires?'

'Of course not. It's just that—that I feel as if I've abandoned her. Marrying so suddenly. There's so many things she doesn't know. She's so innocent.'

'No woman of eighteen is innocent any more. If you ask me . . .'

'Well, I didn't ask you, did I?' Maggie interrupted, close to tears. First Nick had accused her of coddling Bayard and now he was criticising the way she treated Julie. What made him such an authority on bringing up teenagers? 'They're *my* family,' she said belligerently.

'And you don't appreciate any advice from a stranger, is that it?'

Maggie shifted uneasily in the bed. Nick's voice was so cold and unfriendly in the dark. 'I didn't say that. I . . . I appreciate your wanting to help, but I can handle the situation myself.'

'You don't even know what the situation is,' Nick said drily.

'And what does that mean?' Maggie cried.

'It means I'm too tired to argue with you tonight. Go to sleep.'

Maggie lay in silence pondering Nick's words. She didn't want him to believe that his opinions were no more important to her than a stranger's. He was simply much too busy to be bothered with the petty problems of her family. 'Let me explain,' she began. A soft snore came from the other side of the bed.

The pillow was a block of wood beneath her head. Nick couldn't be too upset. He was asleep, his body turned away from her, his back barely brushing her hip. Maggie swallowed a hysterical giggle. She had been married two days and her husband was too tired.

Worried that Nick would continue his criticism, Maggie was nervous about joining him at breakfast the next morning. She worried needlessly. Whatever Nick's sentiments were the night before, they had apparently vanished with the rising sun. An outsider viewing them would have been positive that they had been married for years as they sat at the table discussing the day's weather forecast.

'I hate to run off and leave you with the dishes,' Nick said as he stood.

'Sure you do.'

He grinned. 'Ellen and John will be back tomorrow.' At Maggie's blank look, he added, 'John picked us up in Denver. He drives for me, does the yard work and all the handy-man type stuff around the house. Ellen, his wife, comes in daily to clean the house and cook dinner.

'Surely you don't need someone to clean and cook now that I'm here.'

'I didn't marry you to get a cook,' Nick said, flicking Maggie lightly on the cheek as he walked out of the back door.

No, you married me because I'm sensible, Maggie thought to herself as she neatly stacked the dishes in the dishwasher. And I've never done a less sensible thing in my life.

The long, empty day stretched ahead of her and she was thankful for the large collection of books that Nick had amassed. Some of them had obviously been in his family for years while others were bestsellers. Maggie couldn't imagine when Nick found the time to read them all.

The day passed more quickly than she expected. The phone rang once, Maggie's heart beating quicker at the sound of Nick's voice. She could hear the amusement come over the wires when she admitted that she was reading. Nick promised to bring her home a book on Boulder.

He came home early. Immersed in her book, she didn't hear his arrival and the light touch on the top of her head startled her.

'Hi. How about a little sight-seeing drive around town?'

'I'd like that.' Maggie untwisted her legs from the contorted position she read in and stretched lazily. 'Just let me powder my nose.'

Nick plunked his briefcase down on his desk and took off his sunglasses. 'Don't hide all the freckles,' he said absently as he sorted through his mail.

Maggie stared at her freckled face in the mirror. As if she could. What an odd thing for Nick to say. She was still puzzling over it when she joined him in his small, dark sports-car. Mid-afternoon, the neighbourhood was quiet as if the extreme heat of the day had driven all the children inside. The lawns were emerald green, some bordered with gay flowerbeds, others landscaped with rocks and wood. Yellow-blossomed cinquefoil contrasted pleasantly with the quivering leaves and white bark of aspen along Nick's driveway. The cedar-clad house was a successful blend of modern and Victorian architecture, and Maggie delighted in its proportions.

As they drove down the street Nick told her a little about their neighbours. His mouth twisted wryly.

'They're honouring our honeymoon right now.'

'How kind of them,' Maggie said faintly. The mockery in Nick's voice had been unmistakable.

They turned on to a divided street, white petunias and salmon geraniums lending a festive air to the central reservation. Maggie looked about her with interest as Nick pointed out various local sights.

'Here's the University of Colorado,' he said, turning into an area of stately-looking buildings, green vines growing up the soft-looking pink facades. As they would their way between the imposing structures, Nick suggested, 'Julie might like to go here.'

'I think she had her heart set on Arizona State,' Maggie said. 'That's where most of her friends are going.'

Nick shrugged. 'Just an idea.'

Maggie stared wistfully out of the window at the students on the bridge they were crossing over. She felt a hundred years older than the young men and woman laughing light-heartedly, as carefree as the water flowing beneath the bridge. Enjoy yourselves now, she wanted to shout, before you find out how harsh the realities of life are.

After some minutes Nick brought the car to a smooth stop 'Here we are,' he announced.

Puzzled, Maggie looked out. They were in a neighbourhood of enormous old homes. The wide street was divided in the middle, shaded by huge maple trees. Directly beside them a large, rambling white house sported Victorian gables and gingerbread trim, while wide porches reminiscent of southern verandas ran along the front of the house. An elaborate wrought-iron fence surrounded the trim lawn and colourful flower-beds were planted with red impatiens and white petunias. Behind the windows in a handsome two-storey bay window, Maggie caught a glimpse of lace curtains. 'It's a lovely home,' she said, wondering why Nick had stopped here.

'My great-grandfather built this house back in 1892. My grandfather, my father and I were all brought up in it. I'm afraid that a guided tour will have to wait until my sister returns.'

'I can hardly wait. It looks beautiful.' The house gave off an air of stability and majesty. She could visualise Nick as a small child racing around the porches. 'Are you sorry that she got the family home? There must be lots of memories here for you.'

'I'll always keep the memories, even if I don't have the house,' he pointed out.

Maggie eyed the house wistfully. 'It must be wonderful to have the kind of roots you do. From the time the Russells landed on the American shores they were moving from one place to another. Nana said the McPhersons, that was her family, were just as bad. I guess they were always looking for the pot of gold at the end of the rainbow. We lived in Kansas, Oklahoma and New Mexico before we moved to Tucson when I was ten. I never felt as if I really belonged anywhere. As for relatives, I suppose we have them all over the place, but I never knew any of them.' She glanced over at Nick who was staring at the house. 'I guess that's why I'm so reluctant to let Bayard and Julie go.'

He started up the car. 'Now you can start your own family,' he said abruptly.

Maggie stared at him. They had never discussed having children. Suddenly she could picture a miniature version of Nick, dark-haired but with her curls, his determination, her temper—a child to try a mother's patience—a child to steal a mother's heart.

'I'll take you to the public library when we have more time.' Nick interrupted her thoughts.

She looked up to see a low-slung building fronted with cheery flower beds. 'I'd like that.'

'And we'll save the "Mall Crawl" for another day.' He pointed to a brick-paved street closed to traffic on either side of them. 'This is the Boulder Mall. Pearl Street. Half-way down on the right is Ryan's. Our new big store is out at the Crossroads Mall, but we kept the old store, built in 1889, and located our offices upstairs. The bottom two floors are a kind of mini-Ryan's. We're still trying to decide for sure what to do there. We've tossed around ideas from opening a boutique featuring new and unusual items, to moving our designer clothes over here, to revamping it into a high-style grocery store stocking gourmet foods and party goods. One suggestion has even been made to move our children's department over here.' His enthusiasm for the store was in every word he spoke.

Maggie was perceptive enough to see that taking over the reins of a family business wouldn't be the sincecure tht the casual observer might imagine. Although outsiders might be quick to credit family ties for his success, Maggie suspected that Nick had worked hard for and deserved every promotion that he had received.

On their way back to the house, Nick suggested that they stop and pick up something for dinner. The expensive pâté, cold cuts, cheeses and breads that he loaded their car with made her laugh.

'I can see that you've never had to economise,' she said as they pulled into Nick's driveway. 'I would have picked up bolagna and sliced bread.'

'Then it's a good thing that you had me with you. It's time you learned to live a little.'

Maggie stared in disbelief at the bundles that seemed to multiply when Nick dropped them on the kitchen counter. 'If I eat all that, I'll do more than live a little; I'll grow a lot.'

They were laughing and exchanging nonsense as they ate when the telephone rang. Even before Nick answered it, Maggie knew with a sinking feeling who was on the other end of the line. Nick handed her the phone, a quizzical expression on his face. Don't look at me like that, Maggie wanted to scream, she's my responsibility—I can't just pretend she's no longer my sister simply because I'm a married woman now.'

'Honest, Maggie, this is an emergency,' Julie said with a rush. 'And it will only take a minute. I met the most wonderful man at work today and we got talking and well, I invited him over to dinner with Bayard and me tomorrow night and I can't find that gourmet cookbook of Nana's. Do you know where it is?'

Maggie had to laugh. The emergency solved, she hung up the phone and turned to face Nick. He had disappeared, but the dirty dishes had not.

With the kitchen spotless, she found Nick, as expected, deep in paperwork. Taking a book, she went upstairs where she put on the sensible peach nightgown and settled herself in bed to read. Hours passed before she finally heard Nick's footsteps on the stairs. She pretended a great interest in her book.

'Still awake?' he asked in surprise.

The implication that he had been hoping she was asleep bit painfully into Maggie. 'Barely,' she said, yawning widely. If Nick wanted an excuse not to make love to her, she would give him one. Dropping her book to the floor, she settled back against her pillow and closed her eyes. As soon as Nick went into the dressing-room, she opened them. The wall over her head was reflected in the mirror across the room. Maggie frowned at the light patch on the wall. Nick came to stand beside the bed.

'What was hanging there?' Maggie asked impulsively.

He gave her a startled look. 'Where?'

Twisting around, Maggie pointed to the spot over the bed. 'You can see that it's a different colour from the rest of the wall.'

'You're very observant.' Nick slid into bed and turned off the lights leaving the room in darkness.

'Well?' Maggie prodded.

'A picture.'

'Of what?'

'You're nosy, aren't you?'

Suddenly Maggie thought of the posters decorating Bayard's bedroom walls and giggled. 'It was a nude, wasn't it?'

'What a dirty mind you have, Mrs Ryan,' Nick said in amusement. He rolled over and buried his face in her hair. 'Let's see if you can't put it to better use than worrying about pictures on the wall.'

The days soon settled into a pattern. They ate breakfast together, Nick's thoughts clearly on his day ahead. When he could, he came home early and introduced Maggie to more of Boulder. He took her to the main branch of the public library where she was captivated by the way the building bridged Boulder Creek. The drove around the historic cabins of Boulder's Chautauqua, a nineteenth-century resort started by Texans where the patrons came to spend their summers in the interests of both education and recreation. True to Nick's promise they strolled through the Boulder Mall one evening and Maggie looked in Ryan's windows. Nor were the geological sights of the area forgotten. Maggie was duly impressed by the Flatirons, the red sandstone rocks west of Boulder that leaned one against the other, looking much like the early flatirons that pioneer women had used.

On the surface their life jogged along remarkably serenely. If there were no highs, there were also few lows. As each day passed the image of an angry Nick Ryan in the Tucson office faded, to be replaced by the man who had rescued her in the mountains. Maggie told herself that she had the ideal marriage. A charming husband who frequently put himself out to entertain her. A large modern home decorated by a professional and cleaned by others. No more wondering how to pay the bills, no more struggling to make hamburger taste like steak, no more fears. An idyllic life, in fact. So why did she feel so discontented? She had it all. If sometimes she felt as if something important were missing from her life, she simply had to ignore the feeling.

Harder to ignore was the discovery she had made in Nick's chest of drawers. On her way upstairs one afternoon she had intercepted Ellen and taken from her a pile of clean laundry destined for their bedroom. Her own clothes neatly tucked away, she had turned to Nick's. She had never looked in his chest of drawers before and she had felt comfortably domestic as she sorted his socks and smoothed down his shirts. The shock came when she looked for where he kept his handkerchiefs. Neatly folded in one drawer was a delicate cotton batiste nightgown and matching peignoir, the set daintily embroidered with pink and blue flowers. It was designed for a lovely blonde like Julie. Even worse was what lay below it—a rich gold-coloured silk jacquard negligée with a top so scanty it was practically non-existent and a skirt slit up almost to the waist. Maggie had resolutely slammed the drawer shut. They were obviously relics of Nick's past and she wouldn't think about them.

Easily said. Maggie glanced over at Nick and covertly studied him from beneath lowered lashes as he cooked some chicken on the outdoor grill for their dinner. Just the sight of him standing there, a ridiculous apron over his sports clothes, gave her a funny, craving feeling deep in the pit of her stomach. Is that how the woman who had worn the white outfit had felt? What had the woman looked like who had worn the golden nightgown? Glamorous, sexy, exciting? Did Nick still think of her? Even worse, did Nick think of that other woman while he made love to Maggie? For some reason the thought was distressingly painful.

Maggie looked away from Nick. Behind the house a lone bicyclist struggled to push his machine between a couple of large boulders in the shallow waters of Bear Creek. A woman was walking her dog in the green belt that Boulderites had decreed around their city. Further up the hill a couple of children startled browsing deer and the animals bounded out of sight on spring-like legs.

'I'm sorry that I had to cancel our plans for this afternoon. Our buyer from China got in earlier than expected.' Nick squirted some water on a burst of flame. 'What did you do with yourself today?'

'Read. Cut some flowers. Took a walk behind the

house. Watched some birds. Played patience.' She hoped that Nick didn't hear the note of discontent in her voice.

'Bored?'

'Ellen thinks I'm more hindrance than help around the house. "Go and pick some flowers," she says. This house will soon look like a funeral parlour. And while John allows me to cut flowers, heaven forbid I should suggest pulling a weed. You'd think they were his flower-beds,' she added.

Nick laughed as he flipped the meat on to their plates. 'You'd better face facts. They are. When I first moved in I made a couple of suggestions for flowers to plant. John listened very respectfully and went off and planted what he'd intended to plant all along.'

'What did you say?'

'Nothing. By then I'd discovered that what I wanted him to plant only grows in semi-tropical climates.'

Maggie smiled. 'He might have told you.'

'John doesn't figure it's his place to argue with his boss. And I learned my lesson. He knows his job and I leave him alone to do it. Result—I have some of the loveliest flower-beds in town.' He glanced over at her, fork in mid-air. 'If you are really interested in gardening, I'll talk to John.'

'No,' Maggie said hastily. 'It's just something to do.'

'I thought you were the one who wanted to escape. Get away from the rest of the world. No blaring music. No television. No responsibilities.'

A rueful expression crossed her face. 'I guess I never thought about how empty such a life could be.'

'Why don't you do a little sight-seeing on your

own? You've hardly been outside the house except with me. Run up to the National Centre for Atmospheric Research. Their computers are fascinating, and they have guided tours as well as letting you wander around on your own?'

'What's atmospheric research?'

'See that large pinkish building up on the hill?' He shaded his eyes with his hands. 'They study all kinds of things that have to do with the atmosphere. There are hiking-trails up there as well.'

'It looks like a pretty good hike just to get up there,' Maggie said doubtfully. 'I'm still not acclimatised to this high altitude.'

'Have John drive you up in the car.'

'Oh, sure. Can't you see me descending from the car in front of the laboratory, trailing my fur coat behind me as I sweep into the building?'

Nick grinned. 'It's a little warm for fur. Besides, you're welcome to drive my car.'

'Surely you jest? Your sports-car is so powerful, I'm terrified to back it out of the garage for fear it will drive off without me.'

Before Nick could reply to that the front door-bell rang and he went to open it, Maggie followed at a distance. The next few minutes were totally chaotic as a beautiful, tall, black-haired woman swept into the hallway, kissing and embracing Nick with total abandon. Following placidly in the wake of her whirlwind arrival a benign-looking gentleman about Nick's age shook hands with Nick and nodded pleasantly into the living-room where Maggie stood. Both men smiled tolerantly at the woman as she chattered a mile a minute, constantly squeezing Nick's arm as if to punctuate her sentences. Maggie felt her heart being crushed by a giant nutcracker at the warm, loving light in Nick's eyes, the fond, doting expression on his face. Was this the woman for whom the golden nightgown had been intended? Her breath caught as she saw the look of pure adoration on the other man's face. No wonder Nick had lost the woman to this man. What would it be like to be loved so unreservedly?

'And so, I told Matt the minute we landed we had to come straight over here. I didn't call because I didn't want you to put us off. I'm dying of curiosity. Where is she?'

Nick shook his head, laughing. 'Sensible woman that she is, she probably ran and hid the minute you arrived to save herself from having to listen to all your nonsense.'

Maggie's heart thudded to the floor. Sensible Maggie.

'Nicky!' the woman screeched indignantly. 'Don't you start picking on me.' She gave a dramatic sob. 'I rushed Matt over here and we haven't had dinner and the plane ride was terrible and now you won't even let me meet the bride.' She wiped away an imaginary tear with a theatrical gesture.

'Now you've done it,' the other man said in disgust. 'She'll keep me up half the night telling me how you used to pull her pigtails and put snakes in her bed.'

'Only one snake,' Nick objected. He gave the woman a reproving look. 'Have you been exaggerating again, Hil?'

'I wouldn't be exaggerating if I said that you were the biggest beast in nature,' the woman pouted. 'Your wife has probably already left you, and I wouldn't blame her one bit.'

The man named Matt looked over the woman's

shoulder at Maggie. 'I hope you realised what you were getting into when you married into this family,' he said.

The dark-haired beauty whirled about. Spotting Maggie in the living-room, she dashed in, only to come to an abrupt halt. 'Red hair! You didn't tell me that she had red hair. Why, that's just like . . .'

Whatever it was just like Maggie wasn't to know because at that point Nick put his arm around the woman and gave her a warning squeeze. The woman promptly stopped mid-sentence.

'Maggie, in case you haven't already figured it out, I'm ashamed to tell you that this very rude bubble-head is my sister Hilary. And this is her husband Matt Tate. Hilary, Matt. I'd like you to meet my wife, Maggie.'

Hilary promptly stuck her tongue out at her brother before turning to Maggie and bestowing a charming smile on her. 'I'm so happy to meet you. I was devastated at having to miss your wedding.' Reminded of that grievance, she turned back to Nick. 'I still don't see why you couldn't wait until we got back from Europe.'

'Come now, Hil. Have you been married so long that you've forgotten how anxious you were to marry Matt?'

'That's different. I wouldn't let Matt touch me until our wedding night.' Maggie felt the warm colour stain her cheeks as Nick stiffened at his sister's artless remark. Hilary looked from one to the other. 'Oh, dear.' She took Maggie's hand. 'Nick is sure to tell you that one of my worst habits is that my mouth starts going before my brain does. I am so very happy to meet you, Maggie, and I do hope that we can be friends. Please forgive my stupid remark.'

By the time the Tates left hours later, fed titbits from the refrigerator, Maggie had not only forgiven Hilary, she had decided that Nick's sister was one of the friendliest, most charming women she had ever met. She said as much to Nick as she cleaned up the kitchen.

'I knew you'd like her,' he said. 'She reminds me a lot of Julie.'

'You mean she's another butterfly,' Maggie said slowly.

'That, and the fact that she's a bubble-head.' Nick tipped up her chin. 'Incidently, in case you were wondering about her ill-advised remark this evening, I never discussed with her how we met or our abortive sexual activities at the cabin. Why she said what she said, I have no idea. The way she rattles on sometimes, I'm convinced that her head is full of nothing but rocks.'

'She's very nice,' Maggie said hesitantly.

'A heart of gold,' Nick agreed. 'She'll give you the shirt off her back. Especially if it's one she doesn't like.'

'Nick! How can you say that about your own sister?'

'Being related to her doesn't make me blind to her faults,' he said evenly.

'If you're referring to Bayard, I know what Bayard did was horribly wrong. Would you have me erase him from my life because of it?'

'You'd excuse him if he'd stolen the entire store.'

'That's not true. I was furious with him and he knows it.'

'Sure,' Nick sneered. 'So furious you left him your car.'

'What else would I do with it? You're the one who

insisted that we fly.'

'You could have sold it or had it shipped.'

'It wasn't worth selling or shipping. Besides, you already have two cars.'

'Neither of which you will drive,' he reminded her. 'And what about those phone calls from Julie? She's a big girl. She ought to be handling her problems on her own.'

'I know it's hard for you to understand, but they've depended on me for so long . . .'

'Too long,' Nick interrupted.

'Why are you so hard on them?'

'Why are you so soft on them?' he countered. 'You know as well as I do tht they're weak and immature.'

'It's easy for you to find fault. Brought up by two parents, both still living. Plenty of money. You can't understand what their life has been like.'

'Their life? Or yours?' he asked in a caustic voice. 'They're spoiled, irresponsible . . .'

'No, they're not. They have always worked, always held a job.'

'And what did they do with the money they earned?' he asked dryly.

'They had expenses and things. Clothes.'

'Clothes!' Nick said explosively. 'I've seen what's hanging in your cupboard. Julie probably has four times as many clothes as you do.'

'I never cared that much about clothes,' Maggie said coldly.

'No. All you ever cared about is making sure those two ingrates never worried. Did you ever tell them how tight money was? Did you?'

'Of course I did.' Uneasily she remembered how she had always hidden the worst from them. So many times her grandmother had reminded Maggie that she was the head of the house, that she was responsible for the children. Had she taken her grandmother's admonition too much to heart? There had been times when Maggie had been tempted to reveal the cancerous fears that ate away at her, but the knowledge that there was little the children could do to ease Nana's pain or pay the medical bills had always kept her silent. Even when Bayard had finished high school she had never told him the true extent of their debt for fear that he would forgo a college education. Her habit of withholding the worst from them had become so ingrained that, even with the worst of the crisis overcome, she had never disclosed how closely they had skirted disaster. Was Nick right? Had that been a disservice to them?

'Did they ever help you out around the house? Remember me? I'm the man you married. I saw how tired you were when you walked down that aisle.'

'From sleepless nights,' she flashed. 'What did you think? That I was having sweet dreams about my forthcoming marriage?'

'You're changing the subject,' he said tightly.

'Maybe I'm tired of it.'

'No doubt. I wouldn't want to talk about a sister and brother like yours either. Without you to prop them up they'll fall apart. Admit it. They feed off you like parasites. They don't give a damn about you except for what you can do for them,' he said harshly. 'Your brother let you take his punishment and your sister ignored your unhappiness about your wedding just because she wanted to wear a big pink hat.'

Maggie shook her head, stunned by Nick's biting accusations, but unable to refute them without acknowledging that she knew that Nick had expected to see Julie that day in his office. Bayard had refused to hide behind Julie, and he would have refused Maggie's sacrifice, too . . . if he had known of it. 'They didn't know . . .'

'Open your eyes, Red. Julie doesn't have an unselfish bone in her body or she wouldn't keep bothering you on what's supposed to be your honeymoon for her own selfish reasons. And Bayard, he's just the opposite. He probably hasn't given you a thought since you left. You're nothing more than a household drudge to both of them.'

'You don't know what you're talking about,' she said stiffly. Why did Nick find it so difficult to believe that her brother and sister cared about her? Was she so unlovable? He had called her a drudge. Is that how he thought of her? Dull, dependable Maggie. Nothing more than a drudge.

'I'm well aware that you've sent them money.'

'It was my money,' Maggie said swiftly. 'I had one more pay cheque coming. I haven't used any of your money.'

'That's not the point.'

'I know what the point is,' Maggie screamed, her fists clenched angrily at her side. 'You're trying to tell me that I failed them, that I made them weak. You're saying that my own brother and sister don't love me. Did it ever occur to you that Bayard is too embarrassed to contact me? That Julie calls because she misses me?'

'No,' he said brutally.

'I'd rather die than become as hard and cynical as you are. No wonder you don't want a wife who loves you. You don't know the first thing about love.'

'Do you?' Nick stalked from the kitchen.

CHAPTER SEVEN

NICK was gone when Maggie opened her eyes the next morning. Rolling over on her stomach, she subconsciously reached out and caressed the mattress where he had slept. His scent lingered on his pillow and she breathed deeply, seeking comfort in its familiarity. A feeling of unhappiness tugged at her mind and then the memories of the previous night flooded back to her.

Anger had given her the strength to rush upstairs, but by the time she had reached their bedroom the anger had faded to be replaced by unhappiness, and the huge room with its sterile furnishings mocked her lonely confusion. Did all married people fight over such silly little things? Why had Nick been so quick to rip up at her? More than irritation at Julie's telephone calls and Maggie's sending them money was involved. Was Nick regretting that he had married such an unattractive woman? Was he discovering that sensible and dependable didn't make up for red hair, freckles and dullness?

Maggie closed her eyes in pain, seeing herself as Nick must have when he had finally come upstairs and into the dressing-room last night. She had been seated at her dressing-table, slowly, and she had hoped, seductively, brushing her hair over one shoulder, pretending ignorance of the fact that the peach gown had slipped off her shoulder exposing a small, pink-tipped breast. With each stroke of the brush the cologne she had splashed over her body sent out enticing waves of scent. Ignoring Nick, her heart pounding at her daring, she had brushed and brushed. Nick had said nothing, until, finally unable to bear the silence any longer, Maggie had put down the brush and flipped her hair down her back. She could still see the tiny flame that had flared in Nick's eyes as he met her gaze in the mirror. Then he had turned on his heel and left the small room. When she had come into the bathroom, he was already in bed, his back to her side, his light turned off. His message couldn't have been clearer.

Rolling over, Maggie sat up, hugging Nick's pillow to her stomach. His accusations in the kitchen echoed in her brain. Maybe she had spoiled Bayard and Julie, over-protected them, but they did love her. She knew they did. Just because Nick didn't love her, he didn't need to be so quick to jump to the conclusion that she wasn't lovable.

Nick's pillow went flying across the room and Maggie scrambled out of bed. Stripping off her nightgown, she surveyed her naked body in the mirror. No wonder Nick wasn't attracted. Skinny, red-haired, freckled. She was lucky he hadn't laughed at her attempting to play the siren. Shrugging into her robe, she went downstairs.

Ellen had already arrived. Refusing her offer of bacon and eggs, Maggie took coffee and toast out on to the veranda. The day promised to be blistering hot, an unusual heat-wave according to the radio. A broad-tailed humming bird whistled past her ear, the tiny iridescent creature heading for the feeders that Ellen had set up on the other side of the house. Leaning on the railing, and munching her toast, Maggie watched several young robins filling their spotted bellies with small black berries from large bushes growing along the creek. Even from this distance she could see a bee buzzing around the purple top of a late-blooming thistle while a small cream-coloured butterfly floated delicately above the cattails and brown, dried grass lining the creek. The butterfly, so lovely and graceful. Like Hilary and Julie. The bee flew drunkenly over her head, its legs heavy with plundered pollen. There was nothing lovely about the bee.

Far overhead jet trails split the heavens above the strange rock that Nick called the Devil's Thumb. Maggie had to admit that the solitary landmark jutting up aggressively against the clear blue sky resembled a giant thumb. 'Thumbs up to you, too, baby,' she said sarcastically, her voice startling several small finches on a nearby bush into flight. She turned her back to the rock. Thumbs up, an expression of approval, certainly couldn't be applied to her marriage.

'Mrs Ryan. There's a man at the front door to see you.' Ellen's plump face appeared briefly at the deck door.

Who could be asking for her? Mystified, Maggie went to the door.

A young man in overalls stood there chewing rapidly on a large wad of gum. He dangled a set of keys in front of her. 'Mr Ryan said you should drive me back to the car park and I can tell you all you need to know about this baby.' He jerked this thumb over his shoulder.

In the driveway sat a sleek grey sedan. 'What is it?' Maggie asked in surprise.

'Jeez, lady. Don't you even know a Mercedes when you see one?'

'No. Yes. I mean. Why?'

He shrugged. 'You're asking me? The boss just tells me to deliver this to Mr Ryan's missus and I guess that's you. Maybe it's your birthday or something.'

'You mean it's mine?'

By the time Maggie had thrown on some jeans and delivered the young man back to the showroom she had managed to redeem herself in his eyes by attentively listening to his instructions and proving herself to be a more than competent driver. Etching a quick salute, he hopped out of the car. Maggie started from the forecourt. A sharp whistle stopped her and she turned to see him gesturing that he had something for her. Looking around as she waited for him, she noticed a sporty green convertible.

The young man returned at a loping run. Seeing the direction of her gaze, he said, 'Mr Ryan considered that car but changed his mind. Said it wasn't the right car for you. I'll bet if you like it better, he'd let you trade.' Thrusting a map through the open window, he added, 'Almost forgot this. Mr Ryan said to show you where your house is.' A grimy finger pointed to the map. 'We're right here. And this is the public library. He said you'd want to know that.' The last was said in a doubtful voice.

Thanking him, Maggie pulled out on to the street. Turning off the air-conditioner, she rolled down the windows. Heat rushed in, but at least some of the new-car smell was dissipated. After a few blocks she pulled over to a residential kerb to determine exactly where she was.

Turning off the engine was the signal for the floodgates to open and a million questions to spill out. Maggie slowly unfolded the map. Why had Nick bought her the car? Was he tired of squiring her around town? With the car she was no longer dependent upon him for her sightseeing tours. She brushed her hand over the smooth upholstery and blew an imaginary speck of dust from the dashboard. What did she expect? Nick had told her right from the beginning that he wanted a wife capable of entertaining herself. Overhead a large cloud passed in front of the sun, dimming the radiance of the day.

Parking the new car in the driveway, Maggie looked in the garage. Both the limousine and Nick's sports-car were parked there. She went looking for John and told him that she would be picking Nick up after work that evening.

Maggie was a bundle of nerves by the time she finally found a parking spot a couple of blocks from the Boulder Mall. All day she had agonised as to whether she should call Nick or just show up. And all day she had waited for him to call her about the car. Neither had called.

Passing concrete saucers planted with colourful petunias and marigolds, Maggie breathed deeply of air redolent with the scent of popcorn, pizza and chocolate. Several teenagers kicked around a small ball beneath hanging wooden tubs of red geraniums. Women chatted on wooden benches while small children crawled over metal sculptures on a small playground set amidst the brick walls. Their happy cries echoed in Maggie's ears as she walked along peering into shop windows displaying Indian art and clothing and books.

The Ryan's sign was easy to spot. Maggie stopped one shop short of it and stood so that the window reflected her image back to her. Hair pinned loosely beneath a wide-brimmed straw hat and wearing a light aqua sun-dress with matching jacket, she looked cool and serene. Appearances lied. Her stomach was a churning mass of apprehension and uncertainty. Putting off the moment when she had to face Nick, Maggie tugged on her skirt and tucked invisible hairs under the hat. Why was she worried? Nick couldn't still be mad; he had bought her the car, hadn't he?

Reassured, she walked down the block and through the door into Ryan's. The cold air-conditioned air struck her at the same moment as a most unpleasant thought. What if Nick had ordered the car several days ago before their flight?

'Mrs Ryan?'

Maggie turned to see a spectacled, middle-aged woman smiling anxiously at her. 'You are Mrs Ryan, aren't you?'

'Yes, I am.'

Her bewilderment must have shown on her face because the woman quickly added, 'I hope you don't think I'm too forward speaking up like this, but you looked a little lost when you came through the door, and I thought maybe you were looking for Mr Ryan.'

'I am, but . . .' she stopped in confusion.

The woman laughed. 'How did I know who you are?'

Maggie nodded.

'That's easy. I recognised you from the wedding picture that was in the paper. Mr Ryan put it on the employee bulletin board. That's just like him. So thoughtful. He knew how interested we all were in his marriage.' The woman gave Maggie a conspiratorial smile. 'We've been wondering when you'd be down. I win the prize for seeing you first. But here, you didn't come to chat with me. I'll show you to Mr Ryan's office.' Calling over another employee to her cash register, she led Maggie through the store with the triumphant air of a magician who had just produced a rabbit from a hat.

Maggie was keenly aware of the eyes that followed her progress across the floor. Most of the assistants didn't even bother to hide their curiosity. Warm colour began edging up Maggie's cheekbones even as she returned the smiles sent her way. The walk to the lift was a thousand miles long.

'Mr Ryan's office is on the third floor. Second door on the left,' her self-appointed guide said. 'Here's the button. This lift is old, but it's perfectly safe.'

'Thank you . . .' Maggie found the name tag pinned to the woman's dress '. . . Mrs Willis.'

'My pleasure.' Mrs Willis smiled warmly. 'And may I add the entire staff's sincerest best wishes on your marriage to Mr Ryan? He's a wonderful person and I hope you'll both be very happy.'

'That's very kind of you,' Maggie said. Her last view as the lift door clanged shut was Mrs Willis's beaming face.

The store grapevine was very effective. The woman standing in front of the lift when the metal gates creaked open turned out to be Nick's secretary. She ushered Maggie along the hall, assuring her that the entire store wished them every happiness. By the time Maggie reached Nick's office, all worries about Nick had fled in her haste to escape his well-meaning employees, and she dashed thankfully into the room.

Only to stop on the threshold. Nick was in the far corner bent over a paper-laden table, a trim chestnut-haired woman close to his side. They turned as one at her precipitate entrance, laughter from a shared joke still written on their faces.

'Maggie?' Nick stared at her in surprise.

'I told John I'd give you a lift home,' she said breathlessly, her eyes on the other woman. A woman so chic, so perfect for the golden negligée that Maggie knew instantly that it had been purchased with this woman in mind.

Nick crossed the room to where she still stood in the doorway and guided her into the room, shutting the door behind her. 'You ran in here as if you were running from the police.'

'Worse. I was running the gauntlet.'

Nick gave her a puzzled look which quickly changed to one of understanding. 'I take it you were recognised.'

'Unfortunately, yes.' She smiled up at him in relief. If he'd been cross, there was no evidence of it now. 'I haven't had that many eyes on me since the day a student managed to glue a sign to my back at school without my knowing about it.'

Nick's eyes twinkled down at her. 'What did it say?'

' "Kiss me, I'm Irish." It was St Patrick's day,' she added in explanation.

'Did anyone?'

'The boys' basketball coach in front of his whole team. Just before he took it off and handed it to me.'

'I'll bet the whole team cheered.'

'And whistled and stomped their feet. I thought I'd die.'

Nick put his arms on her shoulders and turned her in a complete circle. 'Just what I thought.'

'What?'

'A sign.' He tipped her face up to his. His lips were warm and persuasive.

Maggie clung to the front of his shirt. 'I don't believe there's a sign,' she said, the hint of laughter in

Nick's eyes having a strange effect on her stomach.

'Are you calling me a liar, Red?' he asked softly.

'Yes.'

'Nobody's allowed to call the boss a liar,' Nick said with feigned menace.

'So what are you going to do about it?' Maggie challenged, her arms gliding up and over his shoulders to clasp together behind his neck.

'Should I assume that we are finished for the day?'

The cool, crisp voice came from behind Maggie and she whirled about. Enjoying the teasing banter with Nick, she had forgotten the other woman who now stood watching them, one elegant eyebrow lifted in interrogation. Maggie flushed with embarrassment.

Nick was made of stronger stuff. 'Sorry, Stella,' he said easily. 'You know how it is with newly-weds.' He drew Maggie to his side. 'Darling, this is Stella Reeves. She's our interior decorator at the store. She's also responsible for our house.'

'Isn't that nice?' Maggie said weakly. 'How lovely to meet you.'

'I didn't know when I did it that it was going to be your bridal nest. I hope you like it. I think it turned out rather sensational, myself.' Stella visibly preened. 'Nick made sure that it was written up for the Sunday home section.'

'How nice,' Maggie said again, unable to think of anything else to say.

'We can finish up that project tomorrow,' Nick told Stella.

'Fine.' The woman picked up some papers from the desk. 'Nice to meet you, Mrs Ryan.' There was a secretive, knowing look on her face, as if she knew something Maggie didn't.

'Nice to have met you.' Maggie suddenly felt very warm in spite of the air-conditioning and she pulled off her hat.

Stella's eyes widened as she stared at Maggie's red hair, a glimmer of amusement in her eyes, quickly shuttered when she realised that Maggie was watching her. 'Amazing,' she murmured to no one in particular as she glided out of the door, her well-shaped hips swaying with subtle sensuality.

Maggie turned to Nick in bewilderment. 'What did she mean by that?'

He shrugged. 'Cryptic remarks are Stella's stock in trade. They awe her clients and make them think that she's so much smarter than they are. That way no one ever questions her decorating judgment. Not that anyone would. She's very talented.'

Maggie thought of the cold, unwelcoming atmosphere in Nick's house and said nothing.

'Just let me get some papers together and we can go,' he added.

Maggie wandered over to the window that looked down over Pearl Street. So that was the woman Nick had in mind when he had picked out that sexy nightgown. Maggie had no trouble visualising Stella in it, that same mocking look in her eyes, holding a mile-long cigarette holder, sipping brandy and wearing outrageously expensive perfume. What could have gone wrong between them? There had certainly been no discernible jealousy on Stella's face when Nick had called her darling, obviously for Stella's benefit. Having seen the opposition, had the other woman written Maggie off already?

'Did John bring you in the limousine, Red? Or did you get brave and drive my sports-car?'

Maggie whirled. Nick was standing behind her,

hands on his hips watching her expectantly. For a moment Maggie failed to grasp the significance of his words and his look. Then it hit her. She looked down at the hat that she was twisting in her hands. 'Actually,' she said airily, 'I drove.'

'Any car in particular?'

Seeing a mirror across the room, she walked over to it. 'Just some old grey thing that was parked in the driveway.' She concentrated on tucking her hair under the straw hat.

'Old grey thing? I'll have you know that it's a family heirloom,' Nick said, his face behind hers in the mirror.

Maggie peeped at him from beneath the hat's brim. 'Do tell. And here I thought it was something that you picked up at a rummage sale.'

Nick took off her hat and sailed it across the room. 'There. That's better,' he said in satisfaction.

'Nick! Do you know what that hat cost me?' Maggie wailed.

'No, and I don't care.' One by one the hairpins holding Maggie's hair in place dropped to the floor. 'Now thank me properly for the car and then I'll tell you a secret.'

'I don't believe in bribery,' Maggie said primly. Strong arms pulled her close against his chest. 'Well, if I must . . .'

'I think I like you when you're grateful,' Nick said several minutes later in a teasing voice.

'Don't you mean "obedient"?'

'Maybe I do.'

'Now tell me the secret,' Maggie demanded.

'Thank me again first.'

'Cheater!' Floucing across the room she retrieved her hat before kneeling on the carpet to pick up the scattered pins.

'Leave those.' Nick pulled her to her feet. 'Am I forgiven?'

'For being a cheater?'

'No.' He stared intently down into her eyes. 'For harassing you last night about your brother and sister. I had no business criticising your treatment of them. You did your best in a bad situation. The car is my way of making amends.'

Maggie stared at him in astonishment. At last she found her voice. 'You apologise with a car? Fighting with me could get very expensive for you.'

'I don't expect always to be the one who has to apologise,' he pointed out. 'After all, you spoke some rather unkind words, too.'

'I know I did, and I'm sorry.' She looked up at him in horror. 'I hope you don't expect me to buy you a car.'

'Take me home and I'll show you exactly what I expect of you.' He wiggled his eyebrows and leered down at her.

'Oh, all right,' Maggie grumbled, pretending to be cross. Not that Nick would be deceived after the way she blushed at his suggestion. 'Let me get my hairpins.'

'You don't need your hairpins.'

'Nick! I can't go through the store with my hair flying all over like this. Everyone stares as it is.'

'You're right. All our customers would go home mad because the sales-people would be too busy watching you to wait on them.' He snapped his fingers. 'I have it.' Picking up the telephone, he asked for the footwear department and then asked someone there to bring up a pair of shoelaces.

Over Nick's objections Maggie managed to pick

up all the hairpins. 'I can't just leave them here. The whole store will talk.'

The whole store had already talked. When Nick finally escorted Maggie from his office, her hair deftly tied at the back of her neck with a white shoelace, every employee on the third floor seemed to know of her presence and managed to find some errand that required them to be in the hall at that very moment. Maggie half expected Nick to sweep her past everyone, but instead he courteously introduced her to each person, giving a little personal history as he did. There was not the slightest hint of impatience in his manner. It was quickly obvious that Mrs Willis was not the only Ryan's employee who thought that Mr Ryan was wonderful. At last they escaped to the lift.

'Whew. You weren't kidding about running the gauntlet.' Nick wiped imaginary sweat from his brow. The lift door grumbled open and Nick guided her inside. 'Alone at last, Mrs Ryan,' he murmured in a sensual voice as the door closed.

'Nick,' Maggie said hastily as he lowered his head. She nodded towards the front of the lift. Two bright-eyed little girls, one on either side of the door, watched them with undisguised interest.

The lift started down with a loud rumble. 'Hello,' Nick said to the girls. 'Riding the lifts?'

The girls stared at him with unblinking eyes.

'Don't talk to strangers,' Maggie muttered softly.

He nodded in understanding. 'Right.'

The single spoken word might have been a command because at that second the lights went off and the lift abruptly halted.

'What's happened?' Maggie asked shakily.

'I don't know. Let me see if I can find the

emergency button.'

Maggie could hear his hands moving against the wall panel. A second sound caught her ear. One the little girls was crying. 'Well,' Maggie said brightly, 'what an adventure!'

'I want my mummy.' A pathetic little voice came out of the darkness.

'Hold my hand, Missy. It will be OK.' A slightly older voice spoke bravely.

'I want Mama,' the younger voice insisted.

Maggie could hear Nick talking softly across the lift.

'My name is Maggie. You're Missy and . . .?'

'I want Mama,' Missy repeated in a sobbing voice.

'The electricity is off,' Nick spoke into Maggie's ear. 'Not just our store. They'll get back to us as soon as they find out something. Do we know who's in here with us? if this takes a while, I don't want to have a hysterical mother downstairs.'

'I'm working on it,' Maggie said. She took a deep breath. 'It's a good thing that Archie isn't stuck in here with us,' she said loudly.

Nick recognised his cue. 'Why is that?'

'That big, silly dog is afraid of the dark. You know how other dogs bury bones? Archie buries torches. Just in case the lights go out.'

'No,' Nick said, playing along.

Maggie nodded, and then remembering that no one could see her said, 'Yes, he does, but when I caught him burying all my lightbulbs I didn't know what to think.'

'Why was he burying lightbulbs?' Nick asked.

'Because he'd read a garden book that said if you want tulips to bloom, you have to plant bulbs.'

A little giggle came from the far corner of the lift.

Encouraged, Maggie went on, 'And do you know what he said to me last summer?'

'No, what?' Nick continued to take up his cue.

'He said he itched so would I fleas give him a bath.'

There was another giggle, followed by a sibilant whisper. 'Get it, Missy? Dogs have fleas.'

Maggie smiled in the dark. 'Did I tell you that I got a letter from Archie today?' Not waiting for Nick's answer, she continued. 'He was telling me all about his latest adventure. He was chasing the neighbour's cat and not looking where he was going when he jumped into a basket. And guess what. It was the basket to a hot-air balloon.' Maggie embroidered the story as she went along, coming up with more and more outrageous ideas until she finally brought Archie back to earth. 'Wasn't that a splendid adventure, Nick?'

'It certainly was,' Nick's amused voice came from the dark.

'And now I shall have an adventure to write to Archie about.' Directing her voice towards the corner, she explained, 'Archie lives in Arizona and that's very far away. But he likes to get letters so I shall write and tell him that I was stuck in a lift. I'll tell him "hi" for you, Nick. Would anyone else like to say "hello" to Archie?' Maggie held her breath.

'I would.' The soft timid voice held only a hint of tears.

'And what shall I tell Archie your name is?'

'Missy Heller.'

Maggie crossed her fingers. Half the battle was won. 'Does anyone else in here want to give Archie a message?'

'I guess you can say hello from Nancy Heller, too,

but I don't believe he can read,' a second voice said defiantly.

Maggie sagged against the wall in relief. She could hear Nick on the telephone again telling someone at the other end to page a Mr or Mrs Heller. There was a rustling noise beside her. 'Maggie,' a scared voice said. 'Would you tell me more stories about Archie?'

'Of course I will. Let's just sit down here on the floor.' Soon Archie was off on another improbable journey, while in the lift one small girl curled up in Maggie's lap and another sat huddled at her side. Maggie's throat was getting dry and she was quickly running out of story ideas for Archie when the lights flashed on and the cage resumed its slow downward journey.

Chaos reigned in the store when the lift door opened. A sobbing woman rushed in and gathered up the two little girls. Maggie started to stand and then fell back on the floor with a little yelp. Nick rushed to her side. 'My legs are asleep,' she said in apology, wincing as the surging blood stuck what seemed to be a million pins and needles in her limbs.

Swinging her up into his arms, Nick carried her to a nearby chair. 'Will you be OK here for a minute?'

Maggie nodded weakly. Now that the crisis was past, all she could think about was what could have happened if the lift had fallen for some reason.

The next half-hour there were introductions and explanations all around. Maggie was glad when the excessively grateful Mrs Heller finally took her leave. She relaxed against the back of the chair and let the excited conversation flow over her.

'You should have told her that she had no business letting those children play in the lift instead of giving her a gift certificate and a ride home,' Mrs Willis was saying sharply to Nick.

'I'm sure Mrs Heller learned her lesson. There was no need for me to say anything to her,' Nick said. 'All a lecture would have accomplished was the loss of a customer. This way Mrs Heller will keep coming back and probably bring her friends and relatives.' He turned to answer someone else's questions.

Happy to be ignored for the moment, Maggie looked about her with interest. She had been too embarrassed on her initial foray through the store to notice very much but now well chosen displays and bright, attractive counters captured her attention. Directly across from her was the women's sportswear department and she studied the clothes on the mannequins, her gaze moving slowly from one model to the next. She wondered if Stella had designed the English-looking décor of the department. The miniprint wallpaper, chintz chairs and framed botanicals bore no resemblance to the modern, bare-bones style of Nick's house. Maggie much preferred the former. A large painting drew her eye, and seeing that Nick was still occupied, she walked over for a closer inspection.

An eighteenth-century lady dressed in flowing green had posed for the artist in front of a handsome black horse. Topped by a small green hat with a flowing veil and luxuriant plumes was a head of flaming red hair.

'Her ladyship gives the place a touch of class, doesn't she?'

Maggie looked over to see a woman about her age smiling at her. 'Her ladyship?'

'That's what I call her. Look at the way she stands there with her nose in the air sneering at all us customers who have to work for a living.'

'She does look a trifle aristocratic,' Maggie admitted. 'Who is she?'

The woman shrugged. 'I don't know. Mr Ryan said that both she and the artist are unknown. I've been making up my own stories about her ever since Mr Ryan brought her in last month. All I know is that no woman with hair that colour could possibly be as puritanical as she looks. I'll bet she was the painter's lover. Oh,' the woman slapped her hand over her mouth. Her eyes flew to Maggie's hair. 'I didn't mean to make any personal remarks, Mrs Ryan. It's just a game I play. Giving her a background, I mean.'

The woman's distress was so genuine that Maggie immediately absolved her of any rudeness.

'Ready to go, Maggie?'

Maggie started at Nick's voice. How long had he been standing there listening?

Once they were outside the store Nick suggested that they stop for a drink on the way home, and within minutes they were seated on the mezzanine of a nearby hotel. As Nick gave their order to the waitress, Maggie looked around her. Settees and chairs upholstered in floral tapestry, small marble tables, dark wood, turn-of-the-century prints on the walls and a glowing stained-glass canopy all contributed to the Victorian ambiance. Near the front of the room a trio played easy jazz, the music punctuated by the clinking of glasses and underscored by the low hum of conversations.

'Like it?' Nick was watching her.

'I love it.'

'It's about as old as your wedding dress.'

The waitress returned with their drinks. While Nick paid the bill, Maggie studied the other customers who were dressed in everything from business suits to shorts and backpacks.

'Here's to your smashing debut, Red.' Nick toasted her with his glass. 'Today the store, tomorrow the chain, and next week the world. To Ryan's own heroine.'

'A heroine! What are you talking about?'

'The way you handled yourself in the lift. I shudder to think what would have happened if I'd been there alone with those two frightened little girls. Or if you'd gone into hysterics and made the situation worse.'

'I wasn't so brave,' Maggie said in discomfort. 'In fact I was terrified.'

'So what? You kept your head and you knew just what to do with those kids. Give me a sensible woman every time I'm stuck in a lift.'

'Is Stella sensible?' she asked without thinking.

Nick laughed. 'Sensible to Stella means dating only men with large incomes so she doesn't accidentally fall in love with someone poor. Why?'

'I don't know. She looks efficient.' Maggie gave him a quick smile and changed the subject. Politics, Colorado history, mining lore, wildlife—Nick's interests were far-ranging, and ordinarily Maggie loved their discussions, but this evening all she could think about was how Nick's desire for her body was so easily switched on and off. In his office he had acted like a man who could hardly wait to get his wife home and into his bed. Now it appeared that bedding his wife was the furthest thing from his mond. He might profess to like Maggie in lifts, but he obviously preferred Stella in bedrooms. Wearing sexy negligées.

CHAPTER EIGHT

AN hour later when they arrived home the telephone was ringing. At a gesture from Nick, Maggie answered it. She knew he thought it was Julie.

'I heard about your terrifying experience and I had to make sure that you and Nick were OK.' Hilary's voice came breathlessly over the wire. Before Maggie could assure her that they were fine, Nick's sister continued, 'My spies tell me that you met Stella Reeves. Isn't she awful? She always makes me feel as if my slip is showing.'

Maggie glanced involuntarily at Nick standing in the hall. 'Uh, yes, I did.'

'I get it. Nick is right there, isn't he?' Hilary asked in a conspiratorial whisper.

'Yes.'

'You don't know what a relief it was to me when he married you. I was terrified that woman was going to be my sister-in-law when Nick let her decorate his house. I volunteered to do it for him, but no, he had to have Stella. But that's not why I called. I'm having a party next week and you and Nick just have to come. I know that Nick says you're not socialising yet, but family is different.'

'I'll let you talk to Nick,' Maggie said. She handed him the telephone. 'It's Hilary.'

She was in the kitchen putting the final touches on the dinner that Ellen had prepared when he finally got off the phone.

'I hope you want to go to Hilary's party, because I

162

couldn't get out of it.'

'And if I don't want to go?' Maggie slid a casserole into the oven.

'C'mon, Maggie. She's my sister. I feel obliged . . .' He stopped, a rueful look on his face. 'Did I just fall into a trap?'

Maggie widened her eyes innocently at him. 'Why, I declare, whatever do you mean, Mr Ryan?'

'Cut out the southern belle routine. I get the message. I'm no more immune to Hilary's pleas than you are to Julie's.'

'If you would have admitted that last night, it would have saved you the price of a car,' Maggie said tartly.

'Speaking of which, what do you think about it?'

Resolutely Maggie thrust aside the memory of the frivolous green sports-car. 'It's beautiful, but expensive.'

'I knew you'd look at the price sticker first and buy the cheapest car on the forecourt.' He picked up a piece of tomato from the salad and popped it in his mouth. 'That's why I didn't take you with me.'

Maggie rapped his hand with the mixing spoon. 'There's nothing wrong with economising.'

'False economy,' Nick said. 'This car will last you for years. It's a good, sensible buy.'

'Sensible,' Maggie echoed weakly.

Nick laughed. 'You should have seen the car I almost bought you. A little green convertible.'

Maggie swallowed. 'Why didn't you?'

'I remembered just in time that you told me that red-heads have to be careful in the sun or they burn. What would you do with a convertible? Besides . . .' He gave her an odd look and stopped abruptly.

'Besides what?' Maggie prodded.

'It's nothing for you to dwell on, but this car is safer. An attractive woman, in a convertible. I was afraid that it might make you a target for some hoodlum who might decide that Mrs Nick Ryan would bring a handsome ransom.'

Maggie stared at him.

'Why are you looking at me like that?' Nick asked.

'Like what?'

'As if I'd just told you that you won the lottery.'

Putting down the spoon, Maggie turned to Nick. He had discarded his tie and unbuttoned the collar of his shirt and she fussed with the lapels. 'I just made a discovery.'

Nicks arms encircled her waist. 'What?' His voice was low and laced with amusement.

'I like you as much as I like my new car.' The cleft in his chin was a pathway to his lips.

Several long and lovely minutes passed before Nick backed away from her. 'I think the peas are burning,' he said.

Maggie was so flustered she couldn't remember how to turn off the stove.

Hopefully Ellen won't ask tomorrow how she'd liked the dinner, Maggie thought later as she lay in bed, Nick asleep at her side. The food might as well not have been on the table for all the notice Maggie took of it. All her awareness had been centred on Nick—his firm lips above a dark, masterful jaw bisected by that irresistible cleft in his chin. She couldn't remember what they had talked about, but she remembered blue eyes that danced with laughter. A warm glow filled her thoughts—Nick had bought her the Mercedes because he cared about her safety. She rolled to her side and focused on the modern chair across the room. The chair that Stella had picked out. The glow dimmed.

As the days passed, Maggie came to a decision. Nick had never denied that he had a past and there was no point in Maggie's dwelling on it. If Nick had wanted to marry Stella, he would have. For whatever reason, they had gone their separate ways and it was none of Maggie's business now. The last thing Nick wanted was a jealous wife on his hands. It wasn't as if Maggie loved him. They had elected to continue with this marriage for sensible reasons based on mutual need and benefit. Nick was turning out to be a kind and generous husband, not to mention a charming companion, and even though they didn't love each other, there was a growing respect and mutual admiration between them. Could all marriages say that? And there was certainly no question of their compatibility in that part of their marriage that took place behind closed bedroom doors. Nick was as warm and generous in bed as he was out of it. What more could a wife want?

Maggie simply had to accept her marriage for what it was. If her life sometimes seemed empty and barren, she told herself it was because she was used to living in a house filled with barking dogs and shouting teenagers. She blamed her growing restlessness on the fact that she was worried about what was going on down in Arizona. Bayard had a new girlfriend, rich, according to Julie, and Maggie couldn't get Nick's warning out of her mind that Bayard would steal again if the circumstances were right. Would Bayard feel the need to impress his new girlfriend and made all the wrong decisions again? As for her sister, even over the telephone Maggie could sense that Julie was changing. No longer open and confiding, she was evasive about her activities and Maggie didn't recognise the names of any of her current friends. Gentle probing on Maggie's part had led to angry words and Julie's slamming down the phone.

Maggie cradled the telephone with shaking hands. For the past three hours as Nick worked in his office she had been trying to get either Julie or Bayard on the phone. Finally she had found Bayard at hime and had pinned him down to an admission that he didn't know where Julie was but suspected that she had started running with a fast crowd and going to drinking parties.

Nick found her still sitting by the telephone, staring across the room in blind despair. 'Dark in here.' He switched on an overhead light. 'What's the matter?' he asked sharply.

'I should never have left Tucson,' Maggie said tonelessly.

Nick immedately demanded an explanation and all her fears poured forth. 'And you couldn't bother to tell me any of this?' he asked, his voice etched with acid.

'I know you think I worry too much about them. I didn't want to bother you.'

'Bother me,' Nick echoed in a savage growl, pacing back and forth across the living-room floor.

'Maybe I should . . .'

'Be quiet,' Nick said, glaring at her before he resumed his pacing. Finally he halted in front of her, his eyes narrow black slits looking down at her. 'You are my wife,' he said with deadly emphasis. 'From now on you are to tell me when you have a problem.'

'All right, I'm sorry.' Maggie was too distraught to take exception to his dictatorial tone.

Nick snorted. 'If you're too upset to fight with me,

you're too upset to discuss this now. We'll talk tomorrow.'

Maggie was still awake at dawn the next morning when Nick rolled out of bed.

He looked down and saw her opened eyes. 'I'm going out of town.'

'But . . .' Maggie sat up in alarm.

'I'll be back tonight or tomorrow,' he said ignoring her interruption. 'The office will know where to reach me. We'll talk about your problem when I get back,' he added.

'What am I supposed to do in the meantime?'

Nick stuck his head back through the doorway. 'Wallpaper the house. Just don't worry about Bayard and Julie.'

Easy for him to say, Maggie thought with frequent resentment over the next two days. A person didn't just stop worrying because someone else told them to do so. A million times she picked up the telephone and a million times she put it back. What would she say to Julie? Listening to Nick had been a mistake. She should have hopped on the first aeroplane to Tucson.

And that's just what she would do. Maggie headed for the telephone to call the airlines just as a loud commotion came from outside. Curious, she went to the front door and opened it. Archie almost knocked her down with his enthusiastic greeting. 'Archie, you lunkhead, get down!' Maggie said, fondling his ears as he jumped up, his enormous paws on her shoulders. Maggie braced herself against the door and laughingly evaded his slurping tongue. Before she could question his presence on Nick's front doorstep, Julie was grinning at her.

'Surprise!'

'Julie! How did you get here? Is Bayard here, too?'

'No, just me. Nick flew down yesterday and talked me into coming back with him.'

Maggie looked over Julie's shoulder to see Nick and John removing luggage from the car. 'Nick? I don't understand. Why didn't you tell me?' Maggie asked in bewilderment.

'I'll explain later,' he said. 'Why don't you show Julie up to one of the spare bedrooms?'

Maggie's head was spinning as she showed Julie to a room, her sister chattering artlessly about Nick's unexpected arrival in Tucson, Nick's inviting her to Boulder to live, Nick finding someone to rent part of the house from Bayard, Nick treating her and Bayard to one of Tucson's finest restaurants, Nick making all the arrangements for shipping Archie, Nick suggesting that she go to college here and offering to pay for it, Nick buying them first-class tickets, Nick's car and Nick's driver, Nick's house, Nick's store, Nick's money . . .

Nick had invited Julie to live with them without even consulting Maggie? Maggie's head began to throb. 'Must you chatter on like a magpie? I can't hear myself think.'

Julie's lips quivered. 'Aren't you happy to see me?'

'Of course I am. I . . . I just have a headache,' Maggie said. 'You unpack and I'll go and lie down.'

Maggie had no intention of lying down. She had to talk to Nick. He was in his office on the phone. Archie lay on the rug, his nose resting on the toe of one of Nick's gleaming shoes. He didn't even bother to look up when Maggie came into the room.

Nick saw the direction of her gaze as he hung up

the telephone. 'Poor Archie. The excitement of his first plane trip wore him out.' He looked closer at Maggie. 'What's wrong?'

'Nothing.' Just that you've taken over and disposed of my entire family without a word to me, that's all.

Nick crossed the room in two strides and took her face in his hands, his thumbs forcing her chin up. Penetrating eyes scrutinised every inch of her face. 'Scratch your new car?'

'No, of course not. Why didn't you tell me that you were going to Tucson?' she asked sharply.

Nick's hands dropped to his sides. 'I knew that you would insist on coming along and I wasn't sure what I would find. You were right to worry about Julie.'

Maggie abruptly sat down, her grievances against Nick forgotten. 'Why? What had she got into?'

'Bad company, as Bayard suspected. Incidently, I had a long talk with Bayard, and I don't think you need to worry about him. This new girlfriend seems to be a good influence. But Julie . . .'

'Tell me.' Her knuckles were white as she gripped the edges of the chair.

'She couldn't handle all that freedom without you there to provide a steadying influence.' He glanced over at Maggie. 'You're right. In many ways she is still a child. I intended to come back and tell you all I learned but I decided the quicker I got her out of Tucson the better. The group she'd joined wasn't above experimenting with drugs. Not Julie,' he added quickly at her gasp. 'But it was only a matter of time. Fortunately she hadn't got herself in so deep that I couldn't extricate her with a few well-chosen bribes.' He pulled Maggie up from the chair into his arms. 'Forgiven?'

She looked at him blankly, her mind still reeling under the shock of his words. Julie and drugs. 'For what?'

'Making all those decisions without consulting you first. I thought moving quickly was essential in this matter.'

Maggie shook her head numbly. 'Drugs.' She reached up and lightly touched Nick's face. 'Thank you.'

'Not mad at me any more?' he asked, brushing a loose curl back from her face.

'What makes you think I was mad?'

'Are you kidding? When you walked in here you were so furious your hair was shooting off sparks.'

Maggie concentrated on the cleft in his chin. 'Maybe I was a little annoyed,' she conceded. 'Now I'm just embarrassed. While I sat around here doing nothing but fretting, you solved the whole problem.' She finally found the courage to meet his eyes. 'Thank you.'

Nick's arms tightened, drawing her up against his hard, lean body. 'Don't you think I deserve a warmer thank-you than that?' he asked in a low, sensuous voice.

'You're awfully greedy . . .' Maggie began, but Nick's lips swallowed the rest of her words.

Archie, who had raised his head and pricked up his ears with the tension in the room, laid his head back down on his paws.

'Maggie!' Julie burst into the room. 'Nick told me about your car and I just had to go see it. It's super! Can I drive it?'

Nick's deep kiss left Maggie trembling. Before she could collect her thoughts and answer her sister, Nick spoke. 'No.'

Maggie looked up at Nick, one eyebrow lifted. 'Don't you think you should consult me about who drives my car?'

'Not in this case. I rode with Julie driving in Tucson and felt lucky to escape alive. I'll buy her her own car.'

'Oh Nick, you mean it?' Julie threw her arms around him, and standing on tip-toes, kissed him squarely on the lips.

Nick didn't seem to mind. Giving her a little squeeze, he said, 'Go and get your purse and driving licence and we'll go now.' He smiled indulgently as she left the room.

Maggie rolled back her eyeballs. 'I'm glad you're not going to spoil her,' she said drily.

Nick laughed before dropping a quick kiss on the tip of her nose. 'There's no reason why you should have to share your car or be at Julie's beck and call when she needs a lift. And I can't see her being content with having John drive her everywhere.'

Julie might not be content with John driving her, but Maggie noticed that her sister was certainly content to have Nick assume the chauffeuring duties. The sightseeing jaunts that had given Maggie so much pleasure were now undertaken for Julie's benefit. When Julie invited Maggie along Nick had quickly said that Maggie had other things to do and he brushed off Maggie's offer to take Julie herself with suggestions that Maggie wallpaper the walls or something. As if he was well aware that wallpaper would look hideous with Stella's décor.

Life took on a whole new flavour now that Julie was staying with them. A flavour that Maggie wasn't so sure she cared for. Companionable dinners with quiet conversations, interesting exchanges of ideas about politics and current events or lively discussions about books and films were all past history. Maggie found herself longing for the autumn when Julie would start at university and have her own friends so that she would no longer be reliant on Maggie and Nick for entertainment. She only wished that she could be sure that Nick was as eager for the day as she was. Far from being bored with Julie's juvenile conversation and artless confidences, Nick seemed delighted with her company. The growing number of Ryan's parcels on Julie's bed spoke of the visits that Julie made there. The only time Maggie had been there was the day they had got stuck in the lift. Nick had never suggested that she return. Maggie's thoughts kept returning to the fact that Nick had been attracted to Julie's picture in Bayard's office.

One day on a dreadful impulse that she refused to analyse Maggie had opened the bottom drawer of Nick's chest of drawers. She immediately wished she had resisted the impulse. The youthful cotton nightgown and robe were gone. Pride kept her from asking Julie about them.

Maggie's only consolation was that at night when the lights went out nothing had changed between them. She refused even to consider the possibility that in the dark Nick might be imagining that she was someone else.

When Hilary heard that Julie was staying with them, she immediately extended a party invitation to her, and Julie could talk of little else in the days preceding the party.

'I haven't got a thing to wear,' she proclaimed at breakfast the morning of the party.

Maggie gave her an amused look. 'All those new

clothes?'

'Those are for college.' Julie cavalierly dismissed them. 'Since Nick won't be home until just before the party, why don't we go shopping and buy something new?'

Ever since Nick had left on a trip two days ago, Julie had nearly driven Maggie crazy with her long-drawn sighs of boredom and pacing from window to window. Maggie realised that Julie, never a reader, missed her active social life in Tucson. 'What a good idea,' she said promptly.

Julie drove straight to the large store in the Crossroads Mall. 'This store has a better selection,' she said as she headed for the teenage department.

'You look absolutely beautiful,' Maggie said as Julie twirled in front of her. She held no hope that her opinion would carry any weight as she had been saying the same thing over and over again for the past two hours.

'It has to be just right,' Julie fussed. 'Tonight is my début into society. What are you wearing?'

'I haven't even thought about it.'

'Maggie!' Julie screeched. 'All these people will be dying to meet Mrs Nicholas Ryan. You can't just wear any old thing.'

Maggie stared at Julie in dismay. Julie was right. She would have to buy herself a new dress when Julie had finished.

Julie finishing seemed to be an impossible dream, but then the saleslady brought out a dress that had just come in. A pale pink floral with tiny capped sleeves and a sweetheart neckline, the dress was fresh and lovely on Julie. 'What do you think?' she asked, tugging the bodice into place. Not waiting for an answer, she went on, 'I love it. I'll take it.'

Maggie's sigh of relief came too soon.

'I'm terribly sorry,' the saleslady said apologetically a few minutes later. 'It appears that Miss Russell has already exceded her charge limit and we can't accept this charge.'

Julie paled in embarrassment. 'Nick told me to add up the bills as I went along,' she said guiltily. 'Only the limit he gave me seemed so incredibly high I didn't see how I could ever spend that much.' She gave the dress one last look of longing. 'I'll find something to wear in my cupboard. Let's go and find you a dress, Maggie.'

Maggie's first inclination that Julie doing without the adorable dress would be a valuable lesson in economics was sabotaged by the memory of Julie looking sweet and virginal and about sixteen in the dress. Maggie swallowed her lecture and said slowly, 'Take the dress. I'll pay for it.' Brushing aside Julie's exuberant gratitude, she added, 'I don't want to be rushed into finding the right dress, but Archie hasn't had any exercise today. Why don't you go on home and take him out? John can pick me up when I'm finished.'

Hours later as she studied herself in the mirror, Maggie was still denying to herself that she had bought the dress in order to emphasise Julie's youth to Nick. Her own dress was bought with one purpose in mind—to convince Nick that his wife was not the dull and respectable drudge that he thought her. Gone was Maggie Ryan, prim and proper librarian. In her place was a woman with shoulder-length red hair, trimmed and styled by the best stylist Ryan's had to offer—at the expense of every woman who had an appointment that afternoon. Maggie had been ruthless in exploiting her name in all of Ryan's departments. She would be embarrassed about that later. Right now all she cared about was Nick's reaction.

Unfortunately that was going to be a delayed reaction. A note on her dressing-table from Julie said that Nick would be late; they were to go on to the party without him. She could hardly wait to see the expression on his face when he saw her dress. The metallic printed fabric was an explosion of colour, rich golds, greens, blues, tangerines and yellows, fashioned dramatically into a low-cut draped halter-top and full skirt belted in gold. New make-up techniques enhanced her ivory skin and turquoise eyes while long, glittery gold earrings dangled from her ears. Maggie thought back to her fantasies at the cabin and giggled. Tonight she was definitely the Russian spy.

Julie's reaction was all that one could hope for. 'Why, Maggie,' she gasped, 'I didn't know you were so beautiful.'

If only Nick's reaction was as gratifying. She did not see him arrive at the party, but suddenly a prickling sensation along the back of her spine told her that he was there. There and watching her. Beneath gay greetings and cheerful conversations she could pick out his low-toned voice. She suppressed the urge to go to him. Nick didn't want a woman who clung. Her body vibrated with such intensity that she felt aware of his every move, his every breath. At last the need to see him was too great to deny and she turned.

He was deep in conversation with a svelte brunette, his back to Maggie. Her heart gave a sickening thud. Far from watching her, he probably hadn't even noticed her. He certainly wasn't searching for her, and looked quite content with his present companion. The woman smiled at Nick, a smile so loaded with sensual invitation that Maggie longed to claw her face. She dared not even join them. Nick wanted to be free to dally with beautiful women at parties. Hadn't he said so?

Swallowing the enormous lump in her throat, Maggie turned away, smiling brightly at the man before her. The party that had seemed so gay and witty turned loud and boorish. The smoke from the other people's cigarettes curled around her head, choking her. A drink was spilled on her dress and someone stepped on her foot. When next she dared turn, Nick was nowhere to be seen. The brunette was bestowing her seductive smile on someone else.

It was long past midnight when Maggie tip-toed quietly up the stairs in Julie's wake. Nick had left the party without speaking to her, leaving a message with Hilary that he was too tired to stay. Only pride had kept her from rushing home. If Nick had wanted her to leave with him, he would have asked her. Carrying her shoes so as not to wake him, she padded quietly into the bedroom.

'Have a good time?' The icy tone came as a distinct shock as Nick unfolded his long length from the chair across the room.

Maggie dropped her shoes to the floor with a loud thump. 'Nick! You startled me. I didn't expect you . . .'

'I'm well aware of that,' he said, cutting into her explanation that she expected to find him asleep. 'While the cat's away, the mice will play, is that it?'

'I . . . I don't know w-what you're talking about,' she faltered, quailing before the furious look on his face.

'Don't play games with me. I saw you at Hilary's. Half-naked, throwing your body at every man in the room like some kind of slut.' He stalked closer and outlined the deep V of her dress with a stiff finger. 'Another dress that used to belong to Grandmother?' he asked nastily.

'Nick! What's wrong with you?' Maggie cried.

'You've been putting on a good act, Red. I almost forgot about the money you stole from me at the cabin. But that's the real Maggie Russell, isn't it? How could I ignore the way you suddenly knew so much about sex after our wedding?'

'I explained to you . . .'

'And I believed you, sucker that I am. Even when you did that remarkable strip-tease in my study, I didn't get it. What a dunce I've been. I thought I was responsible for your wanton behaviour in bed. That's a laugh, isn't it? You turn on and explode for every man who touches you. There's a word for women like you.'

The horrible, ugly accusations bounced off the walls, assaulting Maggie as she stood in frozen horror unable to believe what she was hearing. Nick must have been in an accident, hit on the head or hallucinating. Why else would he be saying all these things? 'Are you all right?' she whispered shakily. Reaching out with a trembling hand she lightly touched his cheek. 'Have you been in an accident?'

'An accident, that's rich, Red. That's rich.' He grabbed her hand and twisted her arm behind her, forcing her up against his unyielding body. 'The only accident in my life was meeting you. I should have left you in the snow where I found you.'

'You don't mean that.' She shook her head wildly, denying the nightmare.

Steel fingers imprisoned her head, holding it immobile. 'I'd like to rip that red hair right out by its roots,' he said, his low voice loaded with cruel menace. His voice changed, became colder. 'Why did you cut it?'

Maggie stared at him. A hard tug on her hair brought tears to her eyes. 'I thought you'd like a more fashionable wife.'

'Liar. You knew I liked it long, liked to play with it, liked to wrap it around . . .' He shoved her away from him and she fell heavily on to the bed. He turned his back to her. 'I've been sitting here thinking about what to do.' His voice was cold and emotionless, the voice of a stranger.

'I'll leave,' she said faintly, blinking back the tears.

He gave an ugly laugh. 'No, you won't, Red. Remember Bayard, your brother, the thief. I own you, remember? You'll do as I want.'

Maggie shuddered up at his harsh voice. She didn't recognise this stranger. 'And what do you want?'

Suddenly the anger drained from his face and body. 'Go to bed. We'll talk in the morning,' he said in a deadened voice, walking from the room, his shoulders slumped bonelessly.

'Nick, please . . .'

The door closed decisively behind him, cutting off her plea.

Maggie curled up in a small ball on the bed, too stunned to get up and undress, her mind numbed by the verbal blows that Nick had delivered. Why had he said all those things? There had been pain as well as anger in his voice and she longed to go to him, to comfort him, but fear held her back. Something had happened to hurt him, to cause him to lash out at her in his pain and distress.

If only she knew the cause . . . if only she dared go to him and take him in her arms, soothing away the frown on his face, kissing away his pain . . . if only she dared tell him that she loved him. Love. She had known for some time, but even to herself she had been afraid to admit the truth. Sensible Maggie. What a laugh! She had done the most foolish thing in the world: fallen in love with her husband, a man who had told her from the very beginning of their marrage that her biggest attraction to him was the fact that she didn't love him. Where was her ballyhooed sensible nature when she needed it?

Morning brought neither answers nor relief. The glittering party dress looked tawdry in the morning light and Maggie ripped it from her body and threw it in the dustbin. The gold earrings followed. Dressed in old blue jeans, Maggie forced herself to go down to breakfast. Nick, Bayard and Julie sat stiffly around the table. Eggs and bacon sat untouched at two places. Nick was just finishing his. His shuttered face told Maggie nothing.

Swallowing convulsively, she bid everyone good morning. She had no desire to discus Nick's anger in front of Julie and Bayard. 'Bayard. When did you get here?'

'Last night. I would have come in and told you, but you were busy,' he said tightly.

Maggie threw a quick glance at Nick. Bayard had heard them fighting. 'Is something wrong with your breakfast?' she asked brightly. 'Ellen can make you something else.'

'I won't eat his food,' Bayard said defensively.

'Me, neither,' Julie said in a little voice. 'He can have his car back and all the other stuff. I'm leaving, but before I do, I have only one thing to say to him.'

She stared down at her plate. 'I lied to Maggie yesterday. I told her that you said for her to go on to the party, that you'd meet her there.'

'Maggie, is that true?' Nick's voice cracked the length of the table.

Maggie stared at them. 'Of course. That's what happened. You did come later. What's wrong with all of you?'

'What's wrong, Maggie, is your marriage to him,' Bayard said heavily. 'I should have known . . . I did suspect . . . but . . . I wanted to believe . . . I persuaded myself . . .' He gave Maggie a crooked smile. 'I came to tell you I was getting married, but I guess that will have to wait. You're leaving him, now, today, and going back to Tucson with us.'

Nick gave Bayard a strange look. 'Even it if means prison for you?' he asked.

'No,' Maggie cried. Next to her Julie was sobbing.

Bayard paled, but he thrust out his chin and manfully faced Maggie. 'I don't care if I have to go to prison. I won't let him make you suffer any more.'

'How about you, Julie?' Nick asked. 'Are you really going to walk away from your new car, new clothes and a free college education?'

'Maggie means more to me than all those things,' Julie cried. 'Bayard and I love Maggie. You don't.'

'Yes, I do,' Nick said matter-of-factly.

Three pairs of astonished eyes swung to him in unison. Bayard and Julie began shouting at him, reminding him of all the things he had said to Maggie last night, proof that the entire argument had had an audience. Nick tried to calm the two of them down, finally losing his own temper and joining in the shouting match. Maggie sat in shock.

Nick looked down the table at her. 'Your mouth is

hanging open, Red.'

The less-than-loving words from a man who had just announced that he loved her was the last straw. Maggie burst into tears.

'Everybody out of here, now!' Nick roared.

'But Maggie never cries,' Julie wailed in distress. 'Not when Mama and Daddy died, not when Nana died, not when Bayard took the money. No matter how bad things got, she never cried. That's how I always knew that everything was going to be all right, that Maggie would take care of it.'

Maggie couldn't stop crying. Around her people moved and whispered and all the while huge sobs shook her body. Tears streaming down her face blinded her to the owner of the strong arms that plucked her off the chair and carried her up to bed. Her body grew chilled and she began to shiver. A blanket tucked around her brought on a spate of fresh tears. At last the tears slowed, the gasping sobs turned into weak hiccups and her swollen eyelids grew heavy.

The closed blinds blocked out most of the sun but Maggie guessed that it must be mid-day when she woke. She was alone in the enormous bed. All that had happened flashed before her and she couldn't prevent the sob that escaped.

'Awake, Red?' Nick had been sitting across the room. 'How do you feel?'

'Terrible. Thirsty. Did you mean it?'

'When I said I loved you? Of course I did.' He handed her a glass of water.

Holding the glass with both hands, she drank greedily. Her parched throat appeased, she handed him the glass. 'Why didn't you tell me before?'

He lay down on top of the covers beside her. 'I was

afraid you'd run away, as you did at the cabin. Would the very sensible Miss Russell ever believe that a man could take one look at her flaming hair and fall head over heels in love with her?'

'No. And I don't believe it now.'

'Neither did I at first. I blamed that funny feeling on you red hair firing up my hormones. Sure, I admired the way you made the best of an uncomfortable situation up at the cabin and didn't get all hysterical on me. And from what little you divulged of your background I put together the picture of a woman who was doing damn well coping with the worst that life could throw at her.'

'I wasn't doing that well.'

Nick pulled her comfortably against his body. 'Well enough that I thought you'd make some man a great wife and some lucky kids a fantastic mother. Of course, I had no intention of being that man,' he teased.

'No, you just wanted to sleep with me.'

'Well, I won't deny that, but what I really thought was that here was a woman like no other I'd ever met. I wanted to know more about you. When I woke up the next morning and you were gone, I thought you were walking Archie. While I waited for you to return, I made plans for us to get to know each other, to let our friendship ripen naturally and see what came of it. You can imagine my feelings when I finally realised that you had gone.'

'You must have been happy to have seen the last of me when you got my note about taking your money.'

He gave her a little shake. 'Is that what you think? Would you believe I went straight back to Boulder and began searching for you?'

She turned startled eyes on him. 'You didn't?'

He nodded. 'I thought you'd started to say Tucson once so I had my secretary call up every library she could find in Tucson looking for a librarian named Maggie. I never thought of school libraries,' he added ruefully. 'Without your last name licence bureaus and phone directories were no good to me. The Tucson office got sick and tired of seeing me, I was down there so often hoping to spot you. I even drove over to Tombstone one day. You'd only let slip 'Tu' and I was ready to try anything. It was pure luck I spotted your picture that day on Bayard's desk.'

'My picture!' Maggie sat up in shock.

Nick pulled her back down. 'Why so surprised? Bayard must have told you that's why I wanted to see you.'

'We thought you wanted to see Julie. Bayard said you saw a picture of her.'

'I wonder why he thought that. It was a picture of you in front of a giant saguaro laughing at the camera.'

Maggie remembered the picture. 'That's the nicest thing anyone has ever said about me.' She blinked away tears.

'That you were laughing at the camera?'

'No. That you saw me instead of Julie. She was standing right beside me. That's why Bayard thought you meant Julie. She's the beauty in our family.'

'Julie? She's just another cute blonde, while you are absolutely breathtakingly beautiful. Hasn't anyone ever told you that before?'

Maggie shook her head mutely, too stunned for words.

Nick grinned. 'Probably no one else noticed. The way you wore your hair pinned up and those damn glasses.'

That reminded her. 'If you wanted to see me, why didn't you know who I was?'

'Of course I knew who you were. I just wanted to know what the silly get-up was for. You forgot the only way I'd ever seen you was with your hair all over the pillow or tied back with a shoestring. I didn't realise until I'd spent time with Julie how everyone in your family thought of your red hair as some kind of flaw.' He buried his face in it. 'I'm going to miss teasing you with it,' he said in a muffled voice.

'It will grow,' Maggie said breathlessly. There was too many unanswered questions to allow Nick to side-track her now. 'Why did you marry me?'

'I didn't want to lose you again. When I thought about all the hours I spent searching for you when you were right under my nose all the time . . . I spent the night before you came furious with myself for not gong home with Bayard right then. I was terrified that you'd found someone else. I wasn't about to let some other man have you. You were mine. What a relief when you walked in with no rings on your fingers. Then and there I determined to marry you. I'd make you fall in love with me.'

'Thus the loving greeting when I walked in at the door,' she mocked softly. 'Why didn't you tell me after we got married?'

'Damn it, Red,' he exploded. 'How could I tell you I loved you when you made it so very clear that you married me only to save your precious brother's hide? You were restless; you didn't love me.' He paused. 'You wouldn't nest.'

'I wouldn't what?' she asked, half laughing, half crying.

'Rearrange the house. All my friends complain that when the get married the first thing their wives do is turn the house upside-down, redecorating and getting it the way they want it. But not you. I kept suggesting you redecorate, wallpaper or something. Instead you treated this house as if it was only a temporary residence for you.'

'I thought you liked it that way.'

Nick shrugged. 'Before we got married, I spent most of my time in the office so the furnishings didn't matter to me one way or the other. It was Stella's idea to decorate the house. Rising young executive and all that claptrap. She was right. It was a good advertisement. You wouldn't believe all the furniture we sold after the newspaper featured the house.'

Maggie pleated the sheet between her fingers. 'Hilary thought you let Stella do the house because . . . you and she . . .'

'Me and Stella? Our relationship has always been strictly business.'

'Then who was the nightgown for?' Maggie blurted out.

'What nightgown?'

'The gold one in your chest of drawers. I wasn't snooping,' she said hastily at his start of surprise. 'I was putting away some clean laundry one day and . . .'

'And immediately jumped to a lot of conclusions.'

'Well, it obviously wasn't meant for me.'

Nick laughed. 'That's exactly who it was meant for. Would you believe that I bought you three negliées? I got talked into one set because it was supposed to be so 'bridal' but I was never convinced it suited you and I finally returned it. The gold one had your name written all over it, but the assistant was so shocked when I bought it, I haven't had the nerve to give it to you. The peach gown was a weak compromise.'

'I thought you bought it because it was sensible. I got so tired of hearing you tell me how sensible I am.'

'Sweetheart, that's one of the things I love best about you. Not only sensible, but dependable. I've had it up to my eyeballs with silly women. I love my mother and Hilary, but they're nothing but butterflies; you can't pin them down to do anything or make a decision. They flit from here to there and drive me crazy.'

'I was so jealous when you called Julie a butterfly. A bee seems so, so . . .'

'So hard-working and dependable?'

'Yes.'

'Which is just exactly what I was looking for in a wife. That was the first thing I noticed about you, well, actually, the second,' he tugged meaningfully on a red curl. 'Besides, what's the first thing you think of when you think of bees?' Nick sat up and started unbuttoning his shirt.

'Stings.'

He laughed as his trousers followed his shirt to the floor.

'Nick,' Maggie said in panic. 'About last night . . .'

'I hung up your dress.'

'You know what I mean.'

'You want to know why I acted like a madman.' He sighed. 'After I'd called the house, we finished earlier than expected and I rushed home to find only Bayard here. It didn't seem unreasonable that you'd gone to Hilary's. I know what kind of pressure she can apply, but when I walked in and saw how sexy you looked, and thought that you'd gone to all that trouble for someone else since you knew I wouldn't be there . . . well, I guess it's fair to say a jealous rage came over me. That side of you was supposed to belong to me and me only. I wanted to bust that fellow you were talking to in the mouth so badly I decided I'd better come home. Then I sat here brooding and you didn't come and you didn't come . . . you know what happened next.'

'I don't understand why Julie lied about your message.'

'She explained that to me. Julie is a more social person than you are and she was worried that I was keeping you too close to home. She wanted you to get out and have a good time and she was afraid that you wouldn't go if you knew I wasn't coming home last night.'

'Nick. About Julie and Bayard . . .'

'All taken care of, and don't rip up at me for not consulting you. Even you have to admit that you were in no condition to make a decision.'

'All right. But if I don't like what you've done . . .' Maggie warned.

Nick chuckled. 'As I told you before, Bayard's girlfriend has him on the straight and narrow. A wedding before Christmas, I think. I was hard on him at breakfast but I wanted you to see that both he and Julie care very much for you. I was wrong in trying to convince you that they didn't. Loving you as much as I do, I should have realised that they couldn't fail to love you, too.' He dropped a light kiss on her forehead. 'As for Julie . . . do you remember Mae Willis from the store?' At Maggie's nod, he continued. 'Her daughter has a flat near the university and is looking for a roommate. Mae's daughter is a nice kid and she'll be a good influence on Julie. This way Julie will be close enough for us to keep an eye on, but out of our hair day in and day out.'

'I thought you liked having her around.'

'Whatever gave you that dumb idea?'

'You spent so much time with her.'

'That's because I felt so guilty about dumping her on you that I figured I ought to take some of the responsibility for entertaining her. Usually I just turned her loose in the store with a credit card.' He brushed aside the blanket covering her. 'Enough about those two. They've already taken up too much of my time and attention.' He turned his attention to matters of much more importance.

The mirror across the room reflected their twin images. Maggie could see her eyes, opened wide and brilliant in her pale face. Nick's dark head lay on her breast and she ran her fingers through his thick hair marvelling at its silken texture. What would their children look like? she wondered dreamily. Nick grew more demanding. A stray beam of light pinpointed the pale rectangle on the wall above them. There was one more thing she had to know.

'Nick!' she said imperiously. 'Tell me what the picture was.'

'Don't you know, Red?' The laughing question was muffled by her skin. 'The painting at the store. I saw it in an antique store after we met. With that red hair she reminded me of you. Once I had the real thing, I didn't need her any more.'

'That's why Hilary and Stella made those odd comments about my red hair.'

'Uh-huh. Red, remember my asking you what is the first thing you think about when you think about bees? You were wrong when you guessed stings.'

'I was?'

He laughed, a low and seductive sound. 'It's honey. Bees give you honey.'

'Nick,' she said desperately.

'What is it this time, Red?' he asked, his voice laced with loving exasperation.

'I love you.'

'I love you, too, Red. Now about that honey . . .'

STORIES OF PASSION AND ROMANCE SPANNING FIVE CENTURIES.

CLAIM THE CROWN – *Carla Neggers*————————£2.95
When Ashley Wakefield and her twin brother inherit a trust fund, they are swept into a whirlwind of intrigue, suspense, danger and romance. Past events unfold when a photograph appears of Ashley wearing her magnificent gems.

JASMINE ON THE WIND – *Mallory Dorn Hart*————————£3.50
The destinies of two young lovers, separated by the tides of war, merge in this magnificent Saga of romance and high adventure set against the backdrop of dazzling Medieval Spain.

A TIME TO LOVE – *Jocelyn Haley*————————£2.50
Jessica Brogan's predictable, staid life is turned upside down when she rescues a small boy from kidnappers. Should she encourage the attentions of the child's gorgeous father, or is he simply acting through a sense of gratitude?

These three new titles will be out in bookshops from January 1989.

W❂RLDWIDE

THE POWER, THE PASSION, AND THE PAIN.

EMPIRE – *Elaine Bissell* _____ £2.95
Sweeping from the 1920s to modern day, this is the unforgettable
saga of Nan Mead. By building an empire of wealth and power she
had triumphed in a man's world – yet to win the man she loves,
she would sacrifice it all.

FOR RICHER OR POORER – *Ruth Alana Smith* _____ £2.50
Another compelling, witty novel by the best-selling author of
'After Midnight'. Dazzling socialite, Britt Hutton is drawn to wealthy
oil tycoon, Clay Cole. Appearances, though, are not what they seem.

SOUTHERN NIGHTS – *Barbara Kaye* _____ £2.25
A tender romance of the Deep South, spanning the wider horizons
of New York City. Shannon Parelli tragically loses her husband but
when she finds a new lover, the path of true love does not run smooth.

These three new titles will be out in bookshops from December 1988.

W♥RLDWIDE

Available from Boots, Martins, John Menzies, WH Smith, Woolworths
and other paperback stockists.